MOST
OF

A Short History
of
The North Staffordshire Mines Rescue Service

Fred Leigh

S.B. Publications

First published in 1993 by S.B. Publications
c/o 19 Grove Road, Seaford, East Sussex BN25 1TP.

ISBN: 1 85770 055 4

Typeset, printed and bound by
Manchester Free Press,
Longford Trading Estate,
Thomas Street, Stretford,
Manchester M32 0JT.
Tel: 061 864 4540.

Front cover: The Midland Coal, Coke and Iron Rescue Team
at the Minnie Pit after the explosion, 1918.

Title page: The large Sevres vase awarded to the Holditch
Rescue Brigade by the President of France.

Back cover: No. 1 Rescue Brigade, Goldendale Colliery.

CONTENTS

ACKNOWLEDGEMENTS

John Abberley, *Evening Sentinel*.

Jim McKinnon, North Staffordshire Mines Rescue Station.

Jim Worgan, Chatterley Whitfield Mining Museum.

Keith Meeson, for the narrative of the Diglake Disaster.

Eric Walklate for the extracts from *The Silverdale Post*.

Vic Dodd for 'Child Labour' and 'Gas Outburst at Norton'.

Ken Stevenson for 'The Leek Puddings'.

Geoffrey Baker for 'The Bevin Boy'.

Bill Shenton, Mike Hodgkinson, J. Hutchinson.

The most valiant in action

FOREWORD

When Fred asked me to write this foreword, it was very difficult to know where to begin, as, in my opinion, every man who ever toiled in the bowels of the earth, together with their wives, families and sweethearts, should be regarded as the 'MOST VALIANT OF PEOPLE'.

When man first began mining coal, little did he realise that he was about to begin fighting a war against the very forces of nature. When coal was lying on or near the surface of the earth, nature allowed man to take it without a fight. When he started to dig into the very bowels of the earth to steal her 'BLACK DIAMONDS', she moved all her heavy artillery against him.

She thundered thousands of tons of rock upon his head,
Engulfed him with millions of gallons of flood water,
Faced him with blazing infernos,
Shook him, to his very soul, with fierce explosions and,
Crept stealthily up on him with her deadly gases.

But, as in any well disciplined army, the front line soldier had the comfort of knowing that, immediately behind, 'THE MOST VALIANT OF MEN' were ready, and willing, to come to his assistance.

His fellow miners picked with their bare hands
at the rocks which had buried him.
Plucked him from natures raging torrents.
Turned those same torrents on her blazing infernos.

And in the last resort, that elite group, 'THE RESCUE BRIGADES', were always willing to go, with their self-contained breathing apparatus and hearts like lions, where no other man could hope to survive.

Sometimes they revived him from natures deadly gases or, as was so often the case, carried his lifeless body from her explosive destructiveness, to bring him for the last time into the loving arms of his family.

The North Staffs Rescue Station adopted the following as its motto:

He Holds No Parley with Unmanly Fears,
Where Duty Bids He Confidently Steers,
Faces a Thousand Dangers at Her Call,
And Trusting in His God Surmounts Them All.
(W. Wordsworth, 1770-1850)

The Most Valiant — The North Staffordshire Mines Rescue Team

Yes, all of these must be considered 'THE MOST VALIANT OF MEN'.
I am grateful to Fred, not only for the privilege of writing this foreword, but for placing on record, for generations to come, the history of their forefathers.

Jim McKinnon,
Superintendent,
North Staffs Mines Rescue Station,
Berry Hill Road,
Fenton,
Stoke-on-Trent.

PREFACE

Men of valour, most valiant of men. This book is dedicated to the miners'. To the thousands who have paid the ultimate price to obtain the 'Black Diamond'. To those who have been maimed, and to those whose health has been impaired.

To those who came through it all, now retired but not dismayed, who reminisce of the good days and the bad, of the camaraderie that cannot be excelled in any other trade. Shared the danger, the work, and each others troubles. Found joy and happiness in the humour that only they know and understand.

To those, in this present time who are concerned about their job when the pit will no longer be there to sustain their families and themselves. Like their forebears they will stand together and fight.

There are not many pits left now, where these valiants worked and made this, our nation great with blood sweat and tears, let us not forget them, and remember them with pride.

There are lots of stories yet to be told, the legends of the North Staffs Coalfields, and I must apologise for omitting in this book all the terrible disasters that have happened in this area, it was not an oversight I do assure you, but time and space. I hope to rectify this in a second book of *Most Valiant of Men* in the near future.

1. NORTH STAFFS. MINES RESCUE BRIGADE

The Most Valiant of Men

Greater love hath no man than this, that a man lay down his life for his friends. (St. John, Chapter 15 Verse 13.)

The following history of the North Staffs. Mines Rescue Brigade was written by Station Superintendent Jim McKinnon to mark the occasion of the 80th. anniversary 1911--991.

The original North Staffordshire Rescue Station was opened by the North Staffordshire Colliery Owners Association in a converted house in January 1911. The Chief Superintendent was Mr. Walter Clifford.

There were no training galleries and exercises with breathing apparatus were confined to the men running up and down stairs, and to burning sulphur to represent practices in smoke.

The equipment available at the time consisted of:-

6 Proto Breathing Apparatus.
6 Electric Hand Lamps.
1 Hand Lever Pump (For charging cylinders).
Several Oxygen Cylinders.
A Few Spares for the Apparatus.

No vehicles were available for transport and early records indicate that the Rescue Station relied on local taxi cabs for several years.

In the early years, some colliery owners held breathing apparatus in special buildings at the colliery, and these must be considered to be the first of the modern RESCUE ROOMS. Early on, it was recognised that the converted house was totally unsuitable for use as a Rescue Station, and two cottages at the Berry Hill colliery were converted for use as a Rescue Station in July 1911.

A wooden gallery was constructed at the end of the cottages for practices. The interior of the gallery was on the same lines as most galleries in use at the present day, and was designed to represent as nearly as possible, the conditions underground after an explosion.

Initial training of rescue men resumed, with two teams of six men per day, one day per week for 13 weeks.

In all, at the end of the 13th . week, only four teams were examined by the Rescue Committee and passed as certified Brigadesmen on the 16th. and 17th. of October 1911.

There should have been 10 teams examined that week, but on Wednesday 19th. October 1911, a telephone message was received at the Rescue Station, to the effect that a serious fire had broken out at the Birchenwood Colliery, and assistance was required immediately. Taxi cabs were called, and the apparatus and men were at the colliery in less than half an hour.

Breathing Apparatus

It is by the strangest coincidence, that only the day following the examination and passing out of the first four Rescue Brigades in North Staffordshire, that the above incident should occur.

It is also interesting to note that, before the other six teams could be examined on completion of their 13 week training, they were called upon to be engaged in rescue work with breathing apparatus both at the Birchenwood Colliery fire and also at the Jamage Colliery where an explosion occurred, killing six men, on 25th. November 1911.

Another batch of ten teams commenced training during the above incidents, and by January 1912, a total of 20 six-man brigades had been successfully trained in rescue work, and indeed had been experienced in underground operations.

Whilst work continued recovering the Jamage Colliery after the disasterous explosion, a call for assistance was received from the Hednesford (Cannock Chase) Colliery, where five men were trapped by a furious fire in the downcast pit bottom.

At this time, the Mines Rescue Station had not yet been established for the Cannock Chase Collieries. Although outside the North Staffs. area, the call for help could not be ignored, and the Birchenwood team, with the necessary apparatus and equipment, were rushed off by road in cars to the Hednesford Colliery.

In spite of heroic endeavours, they were unable to save the lives of any of the poor fellows who were imprisoned.

Training of men continued at the Berry Hill Rescue Station, and scarcely a week passed without a call for assistance. By the end of 1913, men from some 40 collieries had been trained in rescue work.

Some of these men were transferred to other parts of the country to become superintendents of the by now, compulsory Rescue Stations.

Early in 1913, a 16-20 H.P. Enfield car fitted with a van body built to a specified design, was purchased for the rescue station.

During 'The Great War' 1914-18, 'Training and quarterly practices were carried out in a systematic manner at the Berry Hill Rescue Station, broken at intervals by attendance at various collieries for bricking up Gob fires, stopping off bodies of gas, attending whilst ventilation was being changed in particularly fiery mines, recovering tools for blackdamp etc, and similar work which falls within the rescue mans programme'.

The above is quoted for an article by Mr. Walter Clifford, chief superintendent of the N.S.C.O.A. Rescue Station Stoke, in the 'Safety News and Chronicle' published in March, 1922.

On 17th. January, 1915, an explosion occurred at the Minnie Pit in which nine men lost their lives.

During the recovery of the Minnie Pit on 25th. February 1915, a fire broke out at the new Hem Health colliery, some three miles distant, and once again two disasters had to be attended simultaneously.

Eleven men were fatally injured at the 'New Hem Heath' disaster.

In 1917, the Rescue Station was moved to Stoke. During he first year in the new premises, another explosion occurred at the Minnie Pit on the 12th. January, 1918, when 155 men lost their lives.

During the rescue operations, Hugh Doorbar, a member of the Birchenwood Rescue Brigade, lost his life due to a faulty valve on his breathing apparatus.

The recovery of the Minnie Pit was a long and arduous struggle, and it took four Rescue Brigades (one of whom who was in charge was the colliery manager) some 19 months to complete.

The above must stand as a world record, even to this day.

Shortly after the Armistice, a Buick ambulance, which had been used in France, was allotted to the Rescue Station. A special body was fitted to the above, and together with the Enfield car, these were the only two vehicles available to the station until several years after Nationalisation.

Great Disaster

After the end of the Great War, there were numerous incidents attended by the rescue service in North Staffs, and rescue station staff and part time rescue brigades at the collieries carried out their duties courageously but without publicity. The incidents are too numerous to details, and I have chosen only one to relate.

On July 2nd. 1937, during a fire at Hoditch Colliery (Brymbo), a series of explosions occurred.

The loss of 30 lives was a great loss to the community, but the mines rescue service suffered the loss of a brigade of part time rescue men.

When the call for the rescue brigade was sent out, two members were intercepted having just completed their shift, one was known to be on the sick list and was not sent for immediately, three others were summoned, but one, who lived some distance from the colliery was late in arriving. This man attached himself to the Hanley Deep Colliery brigade and was one of those killed.

The rescue men who died were:

James Forrester (Captain)	Aged 40	Hanley Rescue Brigade
Thomas Harris	Aged 46	Hanley Rescue Brigade
William Hough	Aged 37	Hanley Rescue Brigade
Samuel Latham	Aged 28	Hanley Rescue Brigade
Fred Howle	Aged 36	Holditch Rescue Brigade

Again, the rescue service, despite the severe loss, operated in a most courageous and efficient manner, the colliery being restored to normal working within a short period of time.

A formal investigation into the Holditch disaster was carried out by F.H. Wynne, C.B.E. B.Sc. H.M. Chief Inspector of Mines and, in summing up on 'The work of the Rescue Brigades', he says, 'The whole is an epic worthy to rank with the best traditions of British Mining, in which stories of gallantry in the face of imminent peril are not lacking'.

Indeed, the Holditch rescue brigade, captained by Ezra Clarke, were honoured by the award from the 'Congress International de Saubetage'. The award was from the President of the French Republic and consisted of a 'Sevres' vase, a medallion and a diploma.

This now has pride of place in Berry Hill rescue station. Ezra Clarke himself was awarded the 'Edward Medal', later changed to the George Cross which marks acts of the greatest courage.

Glorious History

On the closure of Berry Hill Colliery in 1959, the pit head baths building was converted, at a cost of £20,000, into the new North Staffordshire Rescue Station.

It was officially opened in March 1962 and still serves the collieries to this day.

From Berry Hill 1911 to 1991-80 Years of Dedication.

At the outset, the rescue station provided a service to some 40 collieries belonging to the N.S.C.O.A. and to dozens of smaller mines in North Staffs. The workforce at that time numbered over 30,000 and coal production was in the region of 5,200,000 tons. On Nationalisation, 22 collieries came under the National Coal Board, West Midlands Division, No 1 (North Staffs) Area, employing some 16,500 men and producing around 5,1 million tons.

In 1991, there were only two large collieries employing 2,300 men who produced some 3.8 million tonnes. (1991-92). Sine the foundation of the mines rescue service in North Staffs, a total of 2,083 men have been fully trained in rescue work.

During the 'Great War' of 1914-1918, the rescue service in North Staffs also provided instructors for the 'Army School' where tunnellers were trained.

In 1993, although there were only two collieries, 2,300 men and 61 rescue men, anyone who was ever associated with the North Staffordshire Rescue Station can look back with pride and say:

'I was a part of the glorious history of the North Staffs Rescue Station'.

During his research into the history of the North Staffs Rescue service, Jim McKinnon was fortunate to chance upon the following poem. It is signed simply T.L. and he would be most grateful if someone could identify the poet.

One morn in the month of July,
A day I'll remember until I die.
When Staffordshire miners' did their bit,
To save their mates in the Brymbo pit.
Seventy men in the four feet seam,
Were cutting coal by the pit lamps gleam.
When suddenly from the cutter came, a shower
Of sparks and then a flame
The men downed tools and ran from the place,
A look of fear on every face.
But one old man stopped in his tracks,
And called to the rest, I'm, going back,
For we've left two lads inside that fire.
And he went to his death and funeral pyre.

Just then an explosion decided the rest,
And in the pit bottom they said would be best,
To wait for the rescue team from Deep Pit.
It was folly to go back without rescue kit.
And so they came down from the Hanley mine,
And to the fire began to climb,

To rescue their comrades each one of them strives,
And save them they will if it costs them their lives.

Ah life is sweet but those brave men,
Thought little of their own lives then,
For were not their pals inside that fire,
Perhaps dead or dying through lack of air,
But death overtook them without any sign,
A terrible roar swept through the mine.
Their self sacrifice had all been in vain,
For in less than a second, those heroes were slain.

2. A Narrative of a Survivor of the Diglake Disaster

This narrative was hand written by Aaron Mayer in 1895 a survivor of the Diglake disaster.

While I was working at a colliery known as Diglake, a painful and sad thing happened which is still known to everybody in and out of Staffordshire, and which will never be forgotten in the village of Audley.

It was on the 14th. of January 1895 on Monday morning. I went to my work as usual to commence at half past six. Every thing went on as usual, till about half past eleven, when the fellow that was waggoning for me, came and shouted at the top of his voice, that the water had broken in and that we must come out at once and stop for nothing. I was filling a waggon at the time, and I said to my mate, 'Let's get away off as fast we can to the pit bottom'. We did so but, before we had got one hundred yards away we met the water at the bottom of the engine dip. It was nearly five feet deep. I and my mate were compelled to wade our way back up the dip again and go round another road which is called the air road, to reach a higher point up the engine dip. When we got there, we were about five hundred yards from the pit bottom, which was impossible to reach as the water was coming down in torrents bringing every thing before it, timber, waggons and even tearing the lines up. Just at this time we met four more men who had given up all hope of getting out alive. One of the men whose name was Fred. 'Is there any other road of getting out besides this Aaron?' 'Well' I said. 'There is another road if hasn't fallen in'. 'Very well', he said in a crying tone. 'Let's try and get out'. I said 'Alright all of you follow me'.

Which they did. To our surprise the road had fallen in and it seemed impossible for us to get out. Then there was a scene which was heart rending. They all sat down except me. Then Fred offered up a prayer and wanted us to give up and die together. But I couldn't do that, for if there was any means at all of getting out I meant to try. I then started to move the dirt that had fallen in but I could not get on very well. I don't think it would be half a yard in height, the roof was very bad above me, but I kept working at it. The sweat was pouring off me and my legs trembled under me for the water was roaring and dashing down the main dip. It sounded like thunder for there was only four or five yards between us. My mate asked me if there was still any hope of getting out. I said, 'There might be if we could move the fall of dirt before the water got to us'. We all had to work at it in turns for there was only room for one to work at it at once, it being such a little place. We had to crawl on our hands and knees but we didn't give up. We had to work at it for two to three hours never resting for one minute, for we knew that if we got through that it would lead us to a place called the air pit or better known as the Minnie Pit. But we were suddenly disappointed, for we came to where the road was closed and it seemed that all our work had been in vain, for just then the water had gone down the engine dip and had broken some brick stopping down and forced some gas up to us. . . (The narrative now ends presumably lost but the story continues by the evidence given by Mr. John Watts the certificated manager of the colliery). . . . . . .

'I heard someone shout and saw six men on the top of a fall of dirt. I shouted back and made my way over one fall, but when I got over that I saw another fall larger than the first, and the men seemed to be on top of me. I had not been down many minutes before the flame in my lamp began to flare up, that being a sign of gas. I told the men 'You will have to wait a minute lads; I shall have to go and fetch some one else to help me. I went back to the bottom of the Minnie pit and shouted for some assistance. Amos Hinkley and George Rowley came down with great difficulty and we pulled the men out. The names of the men were Aaron Mayer, Tom Murray, Henry Proctor, Walter Mayer, Daniel Locket and Edward Brindley. If they had stayed there ten minutes longer, they would have been suffocated by gas. I could not take my lamp near them and had to work by the light of a lamp some twenty yards away. I went with them to the Minnie pit. When we got there, Mr. Dodd had just sent up sixteen men he had found in the boundary.

We thought we could save no more in that part of the mine and we made for the Minnie pit ourselves. We were wading about in the water trying to get up the pit, when Mr. Dodd heard knocking on the pipes. He and Boulton went as far as they could get to the cross cut leading to No. 1 pit being up to the breasts in water which went deeper as they went on. Mr. Dodd said to Boulton, 'I'm afraid we can't get here' and Boulton replied 'Oh yes, I can swim'. Mr Dodd answered 'Go on then I will follow'. He went to the top of the 8 feet dip and there he found five more men who had got on the top of the engine. Boulton reached them down and handed them to Dodd then started for Boyles Hall Pit. We went next to get to No. 1, but could not as the water was so deep. We all returned to the bank for some refreshment and a change of clothes. . . . .

3. The Diglake Colliery Disaster

On the 14th. January 1895, one of the worst colliery disasters in North staffs occurred shattering a whole community and leaving in its wake heartbreak, poverty and despair.

A tome could be written about the bravery and the story of the disaster. The colliery was situated at Audley a mining village near to Newcastle-under-Lyme.

About two hundred and sixty men and boys descended to work on the day shift and within an hour the pit came slowly to life. The colliers hewing, the loaders busy filling the tubs the ponies with their boy attendants pulling the tubs, empties in full ones out.

PIT DISASTER RECALLED

Colliery officials returning to the surf ace at the Rookery Pit of the Bignall Hill Colliery Co., Ltd., with the coffin in which had been placed the remains of a victim of the flooding disaster a t the Diglake Colliery in 1895.

Recovery of a body from Diglake after being entombed for 38 years

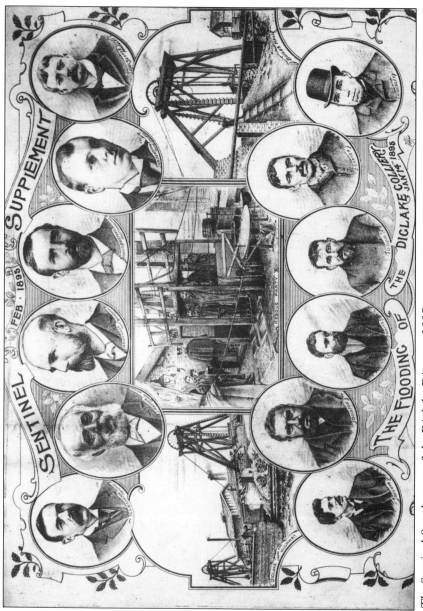

The Sentinel Supplement of the Diglake Disaster, 1895

Young Bill Sproston was one of the boys aged about sixteen and had worked in the pit since he was 12 years of age and worked at the bottom of the dip, hooking on and taking off.

At approximately 11.30 am a noise like thunder startled him and grew in intensity until almost deafening him and within a few seconds the spate of water swept him off his feet together with posts, rails, tubs and other debris. Water from the old flooded Rookery pit had broken through added by the inclement weather from above. Like a massive dam, holding countless millions of gallons of water had been breeched, spewing its contents with relentless fury into the lower regions of the Diglake mine, carrying and drowning everything in its path. Young Bill was carried along for hundreds of yards, helpless against the power that surged around him in complete blackness that enveloped him like the inside of a tomb. He had no time to think or even to pray. then he was aware of a dim light approaching then a hand grabbing him by the hair and being lifted to safety by John Howle.

John Boulton was in his forties, and had been a collier all his working life and had experienced three pit explosions but, he said, that he had never before been associated with anything so sad and horrible as this calamity. The extent of this man's bravery and disregard for his own safety would, if it had happened on a battlefield, have earned him the highest accolade, the Victoria Cross.

He was not at work that day, but after hearing of the calamity he went at once to the pithead. Procuring a lamp he descended the No. 1 pit only to find that the water was at the top of the inset. He signalled to come up again and then descended No. 2 pit and found the same thing there. He then went to Boyle's Hall pit and went down. Mr. William Dodd, the undermanager, had already gone down. He found no water at the bottom of the shaft, and walked about 250 yards to the 10 feet dip and then 60 yards along the level and met John Boulton. At this point they found water. Together they went down an air shaft down which water was cascading. Then they met with a stream of water coming down the dip, and had to return and make their way instead by a back road, and came across sixteen men all huddled together, who had given them selves up for lost. They were given directions how to get out and the rescuers proceeded on their errand of mercy. Understanding that there were others lower down, they went there by the by dip, leaving the water going down the main dip and eventually came upon another six men and these were brought to a place of safety like the others. Boulton then travelled in the direction of No. 2 shaft, but found that he could not get any nearer to it than twenty or thirty yards, the way being blocked by tubs, timber and other kinds of debris. All this time he was wading through water up to his neck. Finding it impossible to reach the No. 2 shaft, he returned and tried to reach the No. 1 shaft when he heard someone tapping on the air pipes. Going in the direction of the sound, he found four men and a boy perched above the reach of the water. Imagine their joy in seeing their rescuer.

Encouraged by Boulton they descended into the water and by the reflection of Dodd's lamp on the water, they were able by wading almost up to the neck in water, to reach a place of safety.

Hour after hour, day after day the rescue teams battled on to try to lower the water level and clear away the debris to reach the rest of the entombed men and boys. A large Cameron pump was brought in, but due to the inlet pipe being constantly blocked with debris, it kept breaking down. By the eleventh day realising that the position was hopeless, with the realisation that the water had never stopped pouring into the mine filling the 8 feet workings and the spate of the water was now backing up and rising up the shafts and it was feared that it would take weeks before any attempt could be made to reach the 7ft and 10ft seams. There appeared no reasonable doubt that the bodies will not be recovered because the probability is that they are buried fathoms deep beneath the accumulated dirt, slurry and debris washed from above into the lower part of the mine.

The full and true story of how the majority of the men and boys were rescued, will never be told. Even the principal actors of this tragedy could not recall the scenes which they took part in without the feeling of remorse and sorrow.

From the very first day the relatives of the entombed men waited patiently for news of their loved ones. The weather was bitterly cold with snow and slush under feet. At night the gas jets that illuminated the pit bank had been put out because of the fear that the foul air and gas emitting from the shaft would possibly explode. The only light was by the miners' lamps that flitted about like the will o' the wisps. There are hundreds of stories that could be told of anguish and despair of the relatives and loved ones awaiting anxiously for news of the entombed men and boys. By Wednesday midnight, hope was till there, kept alive in the breasts of those keeping vigil from Monday. But most now, were persuaded by relatives and friends into the belief that for any to be rescued alive now would be a miracle, and many with the conviction that they would never again see their loved ones. One young woman, however, refused to believe this, and kept a silent anxious and lonely vigil from the engine house. Him whom

DISASTER OF 1895.—The funeral at Audley this afternoon of one of the victims of the flooding disaster at the Diglake Colliery in 1895. The remains, which have not been identified, were discovered recently and brought to the surface on Monday.

Funeral at Audley Church, Diglake Disaster, 1895

she loved so dearly, knew that her man worked in one of the lower levels. The engine-man and the other workman knew of this and tried out of pity for her to persuade her to go home, but she resolutely refused to do this or even to accept and refreshment.

In the home of Mrs. Sproston of Wood Lane, whose husband and two sons were still entombed in the mine, another drama was taking place. She was in a dreadful state of hysteria. She seemed unable to understand any question addressed to her. The distressed woman reclined in a rocking chair and there she sat almost constantly since Monday afternoon. Some half a dozen neighbours were attending her, their presence needed to prevent her going to the pit. Now and again she would declare that she wanted to go to the pit and go below to her husband and lads. Kind words and promises were of no avail, making her friends an exceedingly hard task to restrain her by force when she cried hysterically, 'My poor precious lads. Why wont you let me go to them'. 'Be calm', they told her, 'and we will bring them to you'.

There were so many tragic stories to be told of the 78 men and boys who perished in that mine. The sorrow and hardship of their families lasted for years and will not be forgotten in the generations that follow.

Queen Victoria presented William Dodd the Albert Medal at Windsor Castle on the 9th. March 1895. John Boulton, John Johnson. John Watts, Joseph Bateman, and Amos Hinkley were recommended to receive the Royal Humane Society Award. In 1933 miners' in the adjacent Rookery mine, broke through into the Ten Feet seam of Diglake and recovered three bodies. There still remains some 75 men and boys entombed to this day.

The nation responded and nearly £15000 was raised which was dispensed to the victims dependants.

4. A Gentleman's Gentleman

Joseph Plant was born in a poor district of Hanley. His father and five brothers' were all miners' and worked in the Racecourse No. 3 Pit which was situated off Cobridge Road and now part of the Garden Festival site.

Joe was self educated except for the few years in elementary school. He was an avid reader and a great fan of P.G. Woodhouse and his idol was Jeeve's the valet of Wooster. A burning ambition consumed him that somehow, someday, he would become a Gentleman's Gentleman. It was not easy in the days before the Great War to pick and choose your employment, for there was a well known saying in the area that when you left school you had two choices — 'Pits or Pots'.

Joe was determined, indeed adamant, that under no circumstances was he going to spend his life underground like the rest of his family. His first task was to improve his diction and rid himself of the 'Potteries dialect' and would spend hours alone in the bedroom reading aloud the works of Woodhouse, and his bible was a dictionary, which by the way, was a rare Christmas present given to him by his father who had obtained it by saving coupons from the Daily Herald. He took a party time job after school as an errand boy for a grocery store and the money he received, some three shilling and ninepence a week (19p). He saved this and enrolled in the International Correspondence School who sent his lessons by post and in due course was able to matriculate. He left school at 14 and it was no surprise that he was head boy because he excelled in everything except games.

He was teased by the other schoolboys because of his aloofness and the way he talked. Jeering remarks like 'bighead' and by some even 'Nancyboy'. But Joe was far from being effeminate and could hold his own in the frequent scrimmages he became involved in. This did not deter him from his ambition, on the contrary, it only increased his determination to succeed. 'Well?' asked his father, 'Wot gooin' ter do na yer've left school' Give him his due, his father was very proud of his son's academic achievements and said so and even boasted about him many times.

'They't do well in th' pit lad, a bit moor study an' they could be a deputy, overman, ah if thee plees thee cards raight, oo knows yer could become manager,' Jack, his father, smiled at this, the thought of one of his lads reaching such an exalted position filled him with pride.

'Ah lad, just think on it, manager 'o pit, boss of th' 'ole caboodle. Think on it lad, think on the' 'onour, yer status in the community, and mind lad, the money'. There was a gleam in his eyes and he willed his son to answer in the affirmative. Joe was well aware of his father's good intentions and also of his wrath, for he was a hard man when aroused.

'I'm sorry dad, but with respect, I do not wish to spend my life working in the pit, nor do I aspire to become manager of a coal mine.' Joe answered in a firm matter of fact voice. 'Oh ah', said Jack, the gleam now disappearing from his eyes. 'So wot at gooin' ter do'?

'At a very early age I decided that I wanted to go into service', Joe replied.

'Service!' exclaimed his father. 'Dust mean like thee Aunty Maud, looking after the better off, scrubbin' floors and such?' 'Not exactly. I intend to get some experience in hotels and eventually,' he hesitated watching his father's face beginning to change colour.

'Goo on then. Wot'? Jack asked angrily.

'Eventually I hope to become a Gentleman's Gentleman', Joe said quietly.

'A Gentlemon's wot? And wot th' 'ell does that serpose ter mane'?

'It means' Joe replied rather sheepishly. 'I hope to become a kind of valet to a member of the peerage or some notable. . .' 'They meanst luckin after the bugger wipin' his soddin' nose an' 'is soddin' arse. Ee ah dunner known abite they lad wi' thar brains. Ah saw enough 'o them buggers during the fourtane eightane war thee 'ad wot yer co' batmen. Army Officers thee were serposed ter bey. Officers! Ugh! Thee were nowt but a lot of chinless wonders. Never done a dees work in th' lives'. Jack took his pipe from a shelf near by, filled it and lit it. His steel grey eyes then penetrated the lad standing before him.

'O raight, if that's wot thee wants ter bey, ah anna gooin' ter stop thee.' He said at last, pointing the stem of his pipe at Joe. 'But ah'm warnin' yer. Ah've never shown any favouritism wi' o' me lads an' they wull bey no exception. If yer dunner find werk in two wicks, dine the pit yer'll goo. Ah'll 'ave no layer abites in this family. Dost 'ear me. Ah'll 'ave no idle bugger's 'ere!'

'I appreciate that dad, as a matter of fact, I have a job. I start to work on Monday at the Grand Hotel in Hanley and I am to live in'.

So Joe started at the bottom of the ladder in his chosen career. On his visits to his home he was clean and smartly dressed. His mother fussed over him asking with concern in her voice if he was eating enough, were they treating him alright. By the time he was twenty, he had worked in three large hotels, laboured hard and diligently from boot boy to second waiter so that when the head waiter was absent, Joseph would take over his duties with dignity and all the know how that the post demanded. He could converse with the rich and famous about what wines and food to choose as though he had been born into it. Then calamity struck. The hotel went into receivership and he lost his job. He arrived home with his suitcase, despondent his world it seemed shattered.

Joe spent the next three weeks scanning the Daily newspapers in the Public Library for vacancies then going home and applying for them, the rest of the day he would spend in front of the fire in the living room reading. The taking up of the hearth space was the cause of the trouble that was to come. The Racecourse pit was a wet pit and had no pithead baths, so the living room was used for a changing area and the wet pit clothes put on the hearth for drying. With Joe taking up nearly all the hearth there wasn't much room for his brothers'. He seemed oblivious to the curses and snide remarks and remained aloof and selfish to their demands to move. One day Ted the youngest, was always the first to arrive home. As usual his trousers were covered in mud with the water mark up to his knees. He was wet, dirty and tired and Joe seemed on this day to be coveting much of the hearth.

'Dust think they cost move a bit so ah con take me trisers off and put 'em in front of th' fire'?

Joe slowly turned a page of the book and gave him a disdainful look and continued to read.

'Ah said', repeated young Ted, 'Move thee sel a bit'.

Joe completely ignored his younger brother's request.

Ted had had a real miserable hard day in the pit and could feel his temper rising.

'If thee dustna move an' quick, they't find thee sel in th' strate'!

Joe looked at him with contempt in his eyes. After all, he was four years older than he, of greater intellect a man of the world who had rubbed shoulders with the upper class and was not to be talked to by this. . . this dirty scruffy lad of the earth.

'What did you say'? he asked.

'Yo' 'eard' replied Ted angrily.

'Do you know to whom you are talking'.

'Ah they. Oo dust they think they at eh? wi' thee la de la talk.

They't nite but a nancy boy they at, an' a dee er two in th' pit 'll do they a world a good.'

Joe got to his feet placed the book on the chair and struck young Ted across the face with the back of his hand.

Ted was taken aback at first. He never realised that his brother would resort to violence. Ted was a strong lad, his muscular development helped by two hard years on the haulage in the pit. He lunged forward taking Joe by the throat and toppled over the chair to the floor wrestling frantically. They managed to get to their feet with fists flailing knocking crockery off the table, other chairs and the settle was over turned. Such was the noise, that a neighbour came running in alarmed by the bedlam.

'Stop it!' she screamed 'Stop it!'

Her plea was ignored and she ran from the house for help. Knowing that Jack, the father was having one of his mondays off work and was relaxing with a pint in the pub at the corner of the street.

Anne, the neighbour from next door, burst in the bar. 'Jack!' she shouted, 'Yer'd best come quick. . Theese 'ell ter plee dine yo'er 'ice. Yo'er lads' ah killin' one another!' 'Th' 'ell thee is'. He said rising to his feet and, emptying the remains of his pint in one swallow, ran from the pub. The living room was in a shambles, all the furniture was overturned, crockery strewn all over the floor. Fortunately two of the older brother's had arrived and had parted the offenders.

'Wot the bloody 'ell's gooin on 'ere'! exclaimed the irate Jack. He stared at the two his face red and eyes popping. 'Ah said wot the 'ell's gooin' on?

Young Ted still trembling with anger was being held by his brother, George. Joe was sitting on the upturned settle wiping blood from his nose.

'eh started it' shouted Ted' 'Eh 'it mey cause ah asked 'im ter move 'is sel' from the 'earth so ah could take' me trisers off ter dry 'em'.

'Oh ah', said Jack pointing at Joe, 'An wey didst they 'it 'im eh?'

'Because', he answered still wiping the blood from his now swollen proboscis. Because he was impertinent and called me by an improper name'

'Oh ah an' wot were that?' asked Jack.

'The little snot called me a nancy boy',

There was a snigger form the other two brothers.

'Thees nite ter laugh at', he reprimanded George and Ray.

'An' yo two', he shouted again at the two miscreants.

'Ah'm good mind ter knock yer soddin' yeds tergether. Now get this soddin' place cleaned up afer yer mother comes from up tine or thee'll be soddin' 'ell ter plee. An' they Joseph, Ah'm sick an' tired o' they sittin' by this fire nearly o' dee, Yer've 'ad thray wicks ter find another job, so termorrer ah'll ask Jimmy Ball the manager at pit ter find thee a job. So all beyin' well they't start in th' pit next mondee'.

'There is no way I am going to work down the pit'. Said Joe. 'They, me lad wut do as theet towd or theet get a dose o' this as owd as thee at. Ah've towed yer befoer ah'll 'ave no idle buggers' in this family.' Jack shouted, raising his fist to emphasise his point.

Joe was accepted as another haulage hand and started to work on the following monday at the Racecourse No. 3 pit. After being handed his lamp and told the procedure he reported to the overman accompanied by his brothers'.

'Ah want thee to learn ter drive the engine a top of Peacock Crut'. The overman Tommy Wilson told him. 'Yo'er young Ted 'ill show yer w'ere it is, ah've towd Freddy Rhodes ter show 'im 'ow ter drive it'. By this time Ted and Joe had forgotten their differences so Ted took Joe in hand and told him a few things of what to do and what not to do.

'Wen they gets inter th' cage, owd on ter 'and rail an' wen thee 'ears a bang above thee yed, when cage drops, take ner notice, it's only th'gate droppin'. The cage will drop fast and they't think the ropes brock. Tack ner notice an' grit thee tathe it anna.' Ted informed him.

Joe looked at his younger brother with a sardonic smile. 'And remember, ah youth, dunner ferget ter toke proper. If thee tokes la — de- da lark thee dost at wom, they't get thee leg pulled someit rotten. Dunna they ferget, toke proper mind. Ah shanner bey with thee ter stick up fer the shall ah?

'No Edward I dont suppose you will' replied Joe.

'Theer thee at, toking soddin la- de soddin' la, ah've warned thee anna ah eh?'

Joe would never forget those moments in the cage as it fell seventy feet per second, and feeling the porridge that he had eaten for breakfast come up in his mouth. In those few moments in time he thought of the life he had lived. Those genteel and halycon days and could not for the life of him, why he had given in to his father's demands. The smell of stale sweat, earth, tobacco and other alien odours seemed to permeate his senses making him feel nauseous.

The ringed road from the pit bottom was a surprise to him and young Ted explained the wonders of mining engineering. The endless steel ropes swaying on each side of them, that the empty tubs lashed on to the rope on the left hand side were going in bye and on the right hand side tubs filled with coal were going outbye to the pit bottom.

At last they reached Peacock Crut, likened to a small railway siding with two sets of points in the rails, one for empty tubs and the other for filled tubs. The level of the crut was almost knee deep in water.

'This is weer ah work tackin' off and couplin' up'

'What in all this water'? Asked Joe.

'Ah that's wey me trisers ah o' wet an' muddy wen ah get wom'

'I see', said Joe realising now at least why he shouldn't have been so selfish to the lad a week past, and was near to apologising for his actions but was interrupted.

'They't bey drivin' the engine that pulls the empties up that ah couple on to th' rope an' lets em dine agen wen theer full. So remember ah youth ah'm at th' bottom 'ere an ah've only got this little 'ole, a mon 'ole ter get in if thee lets 'em run awee'.

'I see' said Joe. 'Quite a responsibility'.

'Ah', replied Ted. 'Ah'll tak thee up th' crut ter Fred Rhodes oose gooin ter show thee wot ter do. An' mind ah youth, 'e's a bit of a big yed so mind thee sel', otherwise 'e inna bad youth.'

The crut was about three quarters of a mile in length with a gradient of about 1 in 6 and in places was only high enough for a tub to pass and on one side was a water gutter like a brook allowing the water to get away from the workings. They reached the top of the dip which was now level. A journey of ten loaded tubs were coupled together and ready to be let down. Water, like a perpetual rain storm cascaded down on them. The stationary engine driven by compressed air was partly shielded by a piece of corrugated steel sheet. Fred Rhodes was standing by it awaiting the brothers to reach the landing.

'Ah do Fred, this is ah youth, Joe', said Ted.

'Ah do' replied Fred nodding. 'Ah belave yer've come to learn ter drive this engine.'

'Yes, so I have been. . . told', answered Joe wincing as he received a slight reminder in the shape of a nudge in the ribs by young Ted. 'Ah that's raight', he corrected himself . At the same time looking askance at his young brother, his mentor. "Ere thee at youth' said Fred handling Joe a Donkey Jacket.' Take' the coot off and put this on, it'll keep a bit o' th' wayter off thee. 'Ang thee coot on that nail oe'r theer in that post. it's a bit drier theer'

Joe did as he was told with a nudge from Ted.

'Ah thanks' Joe said looking decidedly uncomfortable attiring himself with this dirty garment. But never the less, he thought, it would help to keep him dry and appeared grateful for Fred's kind gesture.

'Ah'm off', said Ted looking at Joe. They't bey o'raight, luk after thee sel' an' do as they't towd. An' dunner ferget wot 'ave towd thee, wut?'

With this he walked away into the darkness and Joe watched the glimmer of his lamp for a few moments until it disappeared from sight.

'Bob 'ere', said Fred pointing to another youth who had now joined them. 'Does the couplin' up an' the waggonin', W'en 'E's put th' rope on, tuk the lockers ite, eh'll shite raight. Then ah take the slack up on th' rope an' 'eh'll knock them theer blocks ite on front load then it's up ter us.

Fred turned on the air valve and the engine sprang into life. The piston moved slowly and as the drum started to revolve the tubs moved slightly backwards.

Bob moved quickly, taking out the steel lockers and knocking out the blocks and the journey of loaded tubs started to move off the level and down the dip.

Fred's lamp hung just above the rope drum showing the concentration on his face.

'Ah know every foot of this dip', he said 'Wen to goo fast and wen ter goo slow. It's o' theer on the drum thee knowst, by the turns of rope on the drum. . . Na 'ere very slow. cint the turns from this end.' He indicated by spitting a stream of tobacco juice from his mouth, the spray catching in Joe's eyes making him wince,' Na yer can let the buggers goo a bit', he continued, his leg on the brake pedal moving up and down, as he controlled the tubs rate of descent.

'It's experience thee knowst Joe. They't get used to it in time. Thee fost job ah want thee ter do youth', he said, his eyes never leaving the revolving drum. He spat again clearing his mouth of the surplus tobacco juice.

'Is ter notice the noises coming from this 'ere engine. lark squeeks and grindin' fer want o'a bit o' oil and grase. And went wey brote up the journey a tubs, ah wants they ter oil an' grase 'em. O raight youth?'

'Ah o' raight', replied Joe not for getting the tutoring from his brother and looking intently for all the squeeks and other extraneous noises.

'Wey're nearin'the bottom of the dip na, we're yo youth stands weetin', said Fred putting more weight on the brake pedal till the drum on the engine revolved very slowly.

'Ow der yer know? asked Joe.

'They sey'st that chalk mark on th' rope?'

'Yes I see', replied Joe forgetting the dialect.

'Wen that reaches a certain position. . . . theer na wee'r it is na. . . sey.' Fred put more weight on the brake pedal and the drum stopped. 'The journey is just above the' points weer yo' youth stands. 'Is mate is on the main road, an' wen it's clear 'Eh'll signal ter yoer youth wi; 'is lamp. Yo'er youth 'ill then ring twace on th' bell theer luck, just above thee yed then we'll let the buggers goo lark 'ell through the waiter along the level so that yo'er youth dunner 'ave ter push em ite on th' main road. Ast got mey?'

'Yes I see', Joe replied rather perplexed.

The bell above his head rang twice, making Joe jump.

'Thees thee signal' exclaimed Fred at the same time lifting his foot off the brake pedal. The drum started to revolve slowly at first and within a few seconds reached maximum speed. Fred then started to apply the brake again when the rope started to go slack.

'That's it' said Fred, 'Journeys end. Yo youth 'ill take the rope off and couple it on ter the empties.'

The bell above their heads rang three times.

'That's yoer youth tellin' us ter drow up. One ter stop, two ter let dine and thray ter drow up', Fred explained.

He turned on the valve slowly and the pistons with a loud hissing sound started to move making the drum revolve taking up the slack in the rope. The rope tightened taking the strain and Fred opened the valve to increase the compressed air and the drum rotated at a fast speed. It took about three minutes for the journey of tubs to reach the landing. Fred stopped the engine and his mate put in the chock to stop them running away down the dip.

'Na Joe, ah'll give ma mate a 'and ter get thase tubs in and get the loads ite. They cost grase and oil o' the parts that made a noise. Dost remember?'

'Yes I remember', replied Joe taking up the oil can and the can of grease.

The empties were soon moved and the loaded tubs brought to the top of the dip.

'Raight', said Fred taking up his position again on the engine 'Lets bey 'avin' thase dine ter yoer youth'.

The chocks were removed and the journey started on it's way. They started to gain momentum and Fred applied the brake. 'Wot the 'ell!' he exclaimed, his face now contorted with concern and horror. The drum rotated at a very fast speed and Fred had no control. He exerted all his strength and weight, both legs pressing down on the brake pedal and using his arms pressing upwards on the roof support to give added inertia. 'Wot the 'ell ast done ter this bloody engine?' Fred managed to shout. Joe looked on in amazement with mouth agape as he watched the antics of Fred straining his very being trying to control the run aways, 'You told me me to grease and oil every thing that made a noise', Joe shouted at last.

'An' they yer silly sod went an' grased the soddin. . . the soddin' . . . . Bloody brake disna!! Get thee sel on this brake pedal. . . an sprag thee soddin sel lark mey an' soddin quick. Bob!', he screamed.' Come gis us a 'and we've got a runner. Joe positioned himself on the brake pedal. and Bob came running amazed at the two figures antics.

'Get thee sel a post and lever it ter gis us a few mower pinds' This Harry did and smoke started to billow from the brake drum. All in vain the speed of the drum did not diminish. 'If this lot comes off the road at this speed, Thee'll fetch the place in. . . Oh my God!' Joe thought Fred was about to cry, such was the anguish in his voice.

'That poor lad. . . Yoer youth at th' bottom. If it reaches theer an' comes off. . . . Poor Bugger! 'E wunner 'ave a chance. . . an' it's o' thar fault, yer silly sod!'.

Mean while at the bottom of the dip young Ted was unaware of the drama taking place. He stood awaiting the next journey his foot on the rails. He could tell by experience how far the journey was off and the speed they were coming by the vibration on the rails. he realised in a few moments that something was amiss and now he could hear them hurtling down towards him. He shouted to his mate on the main road 'Runners!!' He threw himself into the manhole and covered his head with his arms. In those few seconds in time, his brief space of life flashed before his eyes and then of his mother. Then a roar like thunder as the ten loaded tubs passed him hitting the water on the level making the water rise in the air like a tidal wave. Why the tubs did not shoot the rails now was just short of a miracle. They entered the main road at a terrific speed into a right angle bend and the first tub left the rails, and the others jack knifed into it wedging themselves into the roof. Sparks flew, wood broke and splintered, steel groaned against steel. Coal spewed out heaping all over the road way and the air was thick with coal dust.

It was unfortunate that at this particular time, Jimmy Ball the manager, was walking along the main road from the pit bottom, on his daily inspection and was about 50 yards from the scene.

He ran towards the pile up hoping that no one had been injured. Over the debris he espied Gudder Davies, the taker off. Are you alright Davies?' he asked, giving a sigh of relief. 'Ah ah'mo'raight Mr. Ball, but ah dunner know abite young Ted' 'Well you had better go and see then. How the hell has this happened anyway?' 'Ah dunner know Mr. Ball. It luks ter may lark the ropes brock', answered Gudder. He was about to go and see what had happened to Ted when he saw his lamp moving in the darkness of the crut.

'Ted'! Gudder shouted 'At o'raight'

'Ah' Ted Shouted, Just abite' He emerged slowly into the main road a deathly white pallor showed under the dirt on his face. 'Wot a mess'! he exlaimed looking at the wreckage.

'You my lad, can count your lucky stars young Ted', said the manager.

A few minutes went by when Joseph and Fred appeared breathless from running down the dip.

'Thank God theet o' raight young Ted' said Fred. –'ah thote that they'st 'ad it.

'Well Rhodes what's caused this. . . This mess?'

Fred looked sheepishly at the manager.

'Well, speak up man! Has the rope Broke?'

'Nno, Mr Ball' he took a side ways glance at Joe. 'yer see, Joe 'ere. . . .'

He paused, knowing that Joe would be in very hot water when he told him what had caused the runner, but what could he do.

'Well?' Demanded the manager, 'We haven't got all bloody day, speak up man'.

'Yer see. . . Ah told Joe 'ere ter oil an' grase everthin' that made a noise on th' engine. 'e grased the' brake band on the' drum'.

The manager's eyes popped, his face turned into purple hue, he waved his ramming stick about his head and approached Joe, his intention, it seemed, was to strike him. He was well known for his uncontrollable temper, and was not averse at laying into poor defenceless haulage lads with his stick.

Poor Joe stood there, his face white and still feeling the shock that he could have, through his foolish action killed his young brother.

'And who the bloody hell are you?'

'Joseph Plant', he replied softly.

'It's 'is fost dee in' th' pit' Chimed Young Ted hoping that this would help to soften the wrath. 'Eh did na know any better did 'e?

'Didn't know any better!' raved the manager. 'Only an imbecile would have greased a brake drum and caused all this damage!' He pressed his face close to Joe's, his stick raised above his head.

'Well! Are you bloody dumb as well as bloody daft?!' Joe stood unflinching and returned the stare. 'For your information I am neither an imbecile, dumb or bloody daft, neither can you intimidate me with threats of violence as you are obviously trying to do with that stick. I apologise profusely for the damage I have caused, and in my defence I can only say that I am ignorant of the workings of anything mechanical, especially mining machinery.'

Silence ensued and you could have heard the proverbial pin drop. Jimmy Ball stepped back and lowered the stick, his mouth agape. The onlookers, except for young Ted, bore the same expression of surprise on their faces. Ted had a ghost of a smile on his face and looked at his brother with a new found respect.

'You. . . You. . !' The manager said at last, 'Are fired, get up the pit and out of my sight!'

'Mr Ball, sir,' replied Joe with a flicker of a smile on his face. 'I thank you very much indeed for your magnanimous gesture and, may I say your understanding of the situation. I would reiterate my sincere apologies for being solely responsible for this. . . this wreckage. Sir, gentlemen, I wish you fond adieus' He bowed slightly and made a small flourish with his hand, turned and walked very erect down the main road to the pit bottom.

After an altercation with his father, Joseph left home and made his way to London leaving in his wake, the saga of the greased brake drum, runners and the thespian like way he departed his sojourn it the pit. It was talked about for years, nay, even to this day.

He kept in touch with his family about his career and, one day a letter came from Nice in the south of France, complete with a photograph of Joseph standing by a Bentley with his Gentleman. He had at last attained his ambition in life, to be a Gentleman's Gentleman.

5. Child Labour

In the early part of the 19th. Century, unscrupulous employers eager to make the huge profits that were to be made in the industrial revolution, used every means to achieve their aims. The use of children by these people as a source of cheap labour was widespread and caused an enormous amount of suffering, pain and even death to the victims of these hard hearted avericious people.

One of these pathetic, piteous children was my own great grand father on the distaff side of our family and his story was told to be by my mother.

Although Josèph Woodward worked in the coal mines of North Staffordshire, as an adult, his childhood and youth had been spent in the village of Wrockwardine Wood in Shropshire. Son of a poverty stricken farm labourer whose weekly wage could barely keep his large family alive. Joseph began work in 1835 at a small colliery in Oakengates, he was only 10 years old. He so much wanted to help with the family finances and family history tells of him getting out of bed at 5 am and walking three miles to be at the pit by 6.30 am. In his ragged jacket pocket he carried a frugal amount of food which was to last him the whole 10 hour shift. This my mother told me, very often consisted of a rhubarb foot. This was a little of the stewed rhubarb in a long case of pastry, similar in shape to a human foot, hence the name.

His Job in the pit was a door trapper, which meant that he was to open and close the heavy ventilation doors that controlled the flow of air around the mine workings and through which the coal tubs pushed by the bigger lads passed through. His only illumination a flickering candle. Sometimes, due no doubt to the heat, and tired from his labours and arising so early he would fall asleep. He would be reprimanded severely verbally and physically by the lads pushing their heavy loads, for failing to have the doors open when they approached so losing the momentum when they stopped and having to strain to start again.

Joseph related to my mother many years later, that when he drew his first weeks wages, he was so excited and proud that he could scarcely contain himself. His pay for the 60 hours work was the princely sum of two shillings and one penny (10½p). This was paid to him in the form of one Florin and a penny and he put the coins in his pocket and ran most of the way home eager to give his mother the fruit of his labours.

Tragically, when he arrived, he was told that his father had died suddenly that very morning and that fate had dealt him another cruel blow. He gave solace to his mother in her hour of grief then to give her a little joy searched eagerly in his pocket for the money he had worked so long and hard for. To his dismay he could only find the penny, the florin the most valuable of the two coins, he could not find. In his hurry to get home the coin somehow was lost.

Despite these early setbacks and hardships, Joseph, eventually married and moved to North Staffordshire and worked in various pits. He and his wife, my grandmother, settled in the village of Longbridge Hayes, which has been obliterated to make an industrial estate. He became a highly respected member of the community and like so many upright and decent miners' of that time, became a fervent Methodist. He raised a large family who regarded him with great love and affection before his death in 1898. It is obvious that I never knew him myself, but in my minds eye I very often see him as a small boy trudging to work in the dark down the long Shropshire lanes. With the sweat blood and tears, there were many like Joseph who founded Britain's industrial nation and made it great and they should never be forgotten.

Vic Dodd. Miner, retired. Norton Colliery.

Opening Day, Minnie Pit

6. The Minnie Pit Disaster

The worst colliery disaster in North Staffordshire, occurred at the Minnie Pit, Halmerend, on the 12th. January 1918. The explosion occurred in the Bullhurst seam about 'snappin' time' on a Saturday morning and cost the lives of 155 men and boys. A total of 247 men and boys descended the pit a 6 am that day and a large proportion of the survivors owed their lives to the heroism of Charles Greatbatch a fireman, who displaying a great presence of mind and heroism, and a tremendous risk for his own safety, short circuited the air in his district which enabled his men to reach safety.

This was not the first time that the pit had been subjected to explosions. In February 1898 in the Bullhurst seam, an explosion occurred but no lives were lost. In January 1915, nine lives were lost.

At the time of the holocaust, the manager, Mr Smith was in his office on the surface. He was told that the haulage lads at the pit bottom wanted to come up because something strange and frightening had happened. They said that there had been a sudden fierce gust of wind against the usual air current and pieces of coal, dirt and dust had been blown outbye and they knew something was wrong. The manager then noticed soot and smoke coming from the fan exhaust at the upcast shaft. He immediately went to the fan house and saw that the fan had slowed down. The fan attendant told him that the haulage rope was fast and the engine would not move. Mr Smith telephoned the Banbury haulage and it was answered by Frank Halfpenny who told him that the men and boys there were lying down in the dark, their lamps having gone out. Mr. Smith then told Halfpenny not to let anyone go through the airdoors in the return airway. He then instructed the engine-man not to allow anyone to go down the No. 3 shaft. He telephoned the Central Rescue Station based in Stoke, and requested rescue teams immediately.

The Colliery agent and the undermanager after a brief consultation with the manager, decided to descend the shaft and the manager to remain on the surface to organise the rescue operation.

On arrival at the pit bottom, they found a party of men from the west district who followed the two officials inbye in the direction of the area affected by the explosion. A boy was found dead near the Rearers junction. Three more bodies were found in the entrance to the stables, and nearby, seven men and boys alive but suffering from the affects of the afterdamp. At this point the party divided, one going to the Rearers District and the other down the Banbury Dip. No one was found alive in the Banbury Dip but all the men and boys in the Rearers District were safe.

Mr. Smith, the Manager, meanwhile organised the Rescue Teams and made all the arrangements for receiving and treatment of the injured. The rescue apparatus from the Central Rescue Station at Stoke arrived also the Minnie Pit Brigade fully equipped, and they were told to go as far as they could in the directions of the workings. By noon, all the injured had been brought out by the Minnie Pit Brigade and another team took over. At 1 pm the Minnie Pit brigade returned, and reported a large fall at the entrance to the Bullhurst Crut and, going into the return airway they had observed smoke coming from the Bullhurst seam. On receiving this report, a conference was held and those present were Mr. Saint, H.M. Senior Inspector of Mines, Mr. Henshaw the Managing Director of the Talk 'o' th' Hill Colliery, and other mining engineers and management. It was decided to seal off the Bullhurst seam as a temporary measure because of the Gob fire on that seam. The Silverdale colliery Brigade were given this task. Wearing self contained breathing apparatus they descended the pit at 4.30 pm accompanied by Mr. Bull, Sub Inspector of mines and Mr. Davies the Manager. They discovered that the separation doors between Lockett's Intake and return, had been blown out, but the separation doors about 50 yards inbye were still intact. The brigade took samples of the air in the main return inbye to be analysed later. They returned to the surface at 7.30 pm and taken over by the Burley Colliery Brigade, and on arrival at the Lockett's Intake, where the air analysis had been taken previously, the canary they had taken died instantly. Canvas brattice was fixed across the Bullhurst Main Intake and Return airways. The destroyed doors were also repaired temporarily with brattice. A man, a boy and a pony were found dead at the top of Lockett's Dip. On Sunday, the Rescue Brigades attempted to enter the Banbury Seven Feet workings in advance of the air until 4 pm. It was then decided to carry forward the air with them and at 8 pm Holland's Place up the Push Up was reached where they found three more bodies.

On Monday morning, the Birchenwood Rescue team headed by their Captain Hugh Doorbar were engaged in exploring the Seven feet seam. The team consisted of six men and after consulting with a team coming off duty they proceeded inbye. They reached a fall at the top of Lockett's dip in the Seven Feet Seam, they came aware of a very unpleasant smell. Tests were made for firedamp without result, although a safety lamp burned dimly it was decided to couple up their breathing apparatus. They proceeded slowly and reached a point when their safety lamps went out.

Apedale No. 1 Rescue Team, Minnie Pit

A sharp report was heard and Doorbar was heard to shout, 'Oh my apparatus!' His comrades immediately went to his assistance but he struggled violently. They made every effort to return him to cleaner air, but owing to his violence, he repeatedly knocked off the mouthpieces of those trying to help him and even floored one of them. By this time the team were also affected by the bad atmosphere, and had no alternative but to leave him but by this time they were all certain he was dead. The Birchenwood No.2 Brigade recovered the body at 3 pm the same day. It was discovered later that Doorbar's breathing apparatus was faulty.

The recovery of the bodies was going to be a long and hazardous task because of the devastation caused by the explosion and the ever present gob stink. The work of recovery of the bodies, clearing the falls and building stoppings would have to be carried out by the Rescue teams wearing self contained breathing apparatus.

The exploration of the Seven Feet workings was completed on the 7th. February and all the bodies recovered from that seam. There still remained 98 bodies in the Bullhurst seam. Three were found shortly after at the entrance to the crut. By the 25th. February the Gob stink was so bad and fearing another explosion, it was considered to close the area and suspend all operations. On the 8th. of March, a further inspection was made and it was agreed that the workings were charged with firedamp. March 15th, a

The Chapel at Halmerend where the bodies were taken to be identified

joint inspection, and
that the position was the
same as the week before
and that it would be
unwise to open the
stoppings. The repre-
sentatives of the min-
ers' did not agree, and
that the men would be
willing to reopen the
Bullhurst Seam at once.
It must be borne in
mind that the miners'
were desperate to work,
having received no pay
to feed themselves and
their families. Many had
close relatives still en-
tombed in the pit, and
their wish was for their
release to give them a
Christian burial. This
was refused and after
several meetings and
schemes, the work again
was resumed on July
18th with four Rescue
Brigades. Thirty-four stoppings were built in an atmosphere devoid of
oxygen and step by step the seam was opened up and the last body was
brought out on August 19th. 1919. 20 months after the explosion.

A monument erected near the shaft of the Minnie Pit

Many stories can be told of the bravery of the Rescue Brigades and, the
misery and deprivation to the relatives of the men and boys that perished
in this disaster. The village of Halmerend and surrounding districts still
mourn for the loss of so many of their menfolk and boys.

A memorial was built years later, the names of those that perished
depicted in ceramic tiles. Sadly, vandals of the same age of some of the
boys that died, have desecrated this monument.

7. An Anthology of Pit Poetry

The Lucky Ones

The morning shift had started,
The cage was on its way
Hurtling into darkness,
Away from the light of day.

With Davy lamp and Powder can
We'd walk a mile or more.
Up Jigs as steep as mountain sides
And dips with water and more.

We'd laugh and joke and often spoke
What we'd do if we won the pools,
We'd have a real sunshine soak
And tell the boss what to do with the tools.
But the pools wasn't won
And we soldiered on, lucky to reach sixty five.
For many are crippled and more have passed on
We'er lucky, We're alive.

B.W. Cross

The First Day

I remember my brother held my hand and led
Me slowly up the street.
Though dark and cold the sky tinged with red,
Joining the sombre silent figures we meet,
Boots and clogs with their rhythmic sound,
Echoing in the morning
Arousing the sleeping for their daily round
And another new day dawning.

The pit headgear, a silhouette against the sky,
Like a hangman's gibbet, eerie, cruel.
Perhaps an omen for those to die,
Who take the coal for fire fuel.
The lamphouse shining bright,
And on the bank the lamps lit,
Like fire flies glittering in the night,
Converging slowly to the pit.

In the cage men conversing
And looking at me, small and scared.
A nudge, a laugh, a bit of cursing,
'It be a year this very dee Ted,
When rope broke'. I heard a bell.
The cage plummeted fell,
Into the abyss — Oh God! Amen.

Never felt I the dark so deep,
The velvety blackness encompasses me.
 Hear the timbers above me creak,
As I toil and sweat so eagerly.
My hands are sore my muscles ache,
Oh to rest awhile I pray.
No water left my thirst to slake,
Let there be an end to this odious day.

The shift is o'er, we make our way,
Half a league or so to the shaft.
The cage lifts off to the light of day
And soon, I'm walking so erect,
Breathing air that is clean and pure.
Walking homewards tired and wan,
I lift the latch, open the door
Mother waiting, smiling, 'My little man'.

Fred Leigh

Old Miner's Memories

The heather was purple, the fields were green.
The pit wheels whirled I was jut fourteen.
My trousers were patched, my pit boots odd,
I descended the mine with a prayer to God,
That every day he would keep me from pain
Guide me once more to sunshine and rain.
To me they were heaven, I'm happy to tell,
'Cos down below was just like hell.
The water seeped in t'was smelly and dank,
The light was dim from my Davy lamp.
Around my legs was brattice sheet,
There was no protection from cold cramped feet.
My 'Snap' I twisted in my jacket sleeve,
Yet the 'moggies' still left more holes than a sieve.
They nibbled away at my bacon and cheese,
Imagine my words as I prayed on my knees.
Here I was in a cold damp hell,
Awaiting sweet music 'Lilycock' on the bell.
The pressure was on when I went in the dark,
The 'Davy' I carried had lost all its spark.
There I sat at the foot of the 'jig',
The pit like a a zoo, 'moggies, 'doggies, and pig
Friday noon was the best day of all,
For a hard weeks work the pay packet was small.
They were the days of the hammer and wedge,
A twig in the mouth picked from a hedge.
Down black cheeks have been rivers of white
Made by tears like rain in the night,
Yes they were the tears when my young heart was hurt
When I put on my knee pads and took off my shirt,
There was never no time for a doze or a nap,
Only time for 'moggies to eat all my 'snap'.
I hope they enjoyed my bacon and cheese,
They'd paid their subscriptions 'moggies' union fees

Jack Pagett

Chatterley Whitfield Hesketh Pit, 1952

The Price of Coal

The sun sines down on a mining town,
As men appear from two miles down.
They shield their eyes to ease the pain,
Another shift is done again.
Young men are old before their time,
They should really be in their prime.
Their bodies maimed or scarred with blue,
Full of the fragments of the coal they hew.
Pit wives' have seen the gloom and pain,
Of human flesh that sweats like rain.
The slag heaps loom, and leer and taunt,
What now the price of coal we bought.
When mens' blood flows and life is shed,
So I can go in warmth to my bed.
The old men bent, their lives are done,
When laboured breathing is no fun.
The price of the diamonds we buy by the ton.
Here miners' headstones lean by the wall
We teach our sons to walk straight and tall,
Are they too destined for the dust and grime?
Sweet youthful faces. Will they go down the mine?
The price of coal is high they say,
But not as high as some some men pay.

Doreen McCue

The Miner

Pray tell me no more of the outstanding nations,
Of African Negroes in bondage and thrall;
For slaves may be found amongst all occupations,
But that of the miner surpasses them all.
Behold the poor creatures in groups now descending
Through strata and minerals, undaunted they go,
Where labour and danger together are blending
An emblem of Pluto's dark regions below.
Now doubt, death and sorrow at once are surrounding
They labour together by faint candle light,
Fatigued and naked, with sweat almost drowning
They cruise the earths bowels from morning to night.
Picks, hammers and wedges, now clanging together
Till terror cries echo throughout the domain,
No sun ever cheers nor gay seasons of weather
But labour and danger continually reign.
Hark! Hark! The loudburst subterraneous thunder
Now fills every bosom with terror and woe.
The gearing above is all blasted asunder
Ah, woe to the poor wretched miners' below.
But God of all mercies, who sees in all places,
Forwarned them of danger the moment before.
All trembling and prostrate, fall down on their faces
The fire pass'd above them, and danger was o'er.
But mark the sad contrast, by heaven directed
A little time after, while cutting a wall,
The roof from above them fell down unexpected
And two of the miners' were killed by the fall.
Such are the fruits of the miners' profession,
The fruits of hard labour, and danger and woe.
May the great God of heaven look down with compassion
And sooth the great hardships of miners' below.

John Lumsdon

8. Norton Colliery Explosion

Although only one man died, this could have been the worst colliery disaster in the country. By the grace of God only three men were at work being a Saturday afternoon. The three men were pit fettlers and were working in the shaft.

The call was received at the North Staffs Rescue station, on February 24th. 1912, and, within 23 minutes they arrived at the scene and found that the explosion had been extremely violent. In fact, it was the opinion of most of the mining engineers who saw the devastation, that it was the most violent explosion that had taken place in any colliery in the country. If it had happened just a few hours earlier, over 400 men and boys who had been working there that morning would not have survived. 76 pit ponies perished, their bodies horribly mangled and burnt, not one was found alive.

The atmosphere was deadly, as much as 4 per cent C.O. with less than 1 per cent. of oxygen. The damage at the pit bottom of the downcast shaft was almost indescribable. Full tubs of coal had been blown across the pit bottom, in many cases the bogies cut off as with a huge knife, and thrown some 50 yards. The brick built arches, 6 feet thick were blown out, a large haulage engine and several new electric centrifugal pumps had been smashed to pieces. The separation doors were so broken up and damaged that no piece of wood could be found that was larger than a mans finger. The empty tubs were battered in to all sorts of fantastic shapes, so much in fact that they were now hardly recognised as tubs. To make matters worse for the recovery men the water began to rise in the pit bottom because of the pumps being smashed. The gear at the bottom of the downcast shaft was broken due to a train of empty tubs that had been blown bodily across the shaft, stopping the cages to a point 6ft above the pit bottom. Such was the scene at the pit bottom alone. A huge cloud of smoke was seen coming from the mouth of the shaft, depositing a coat of soot on the head gears. It was decided to descend by way of the upcast shaft which least likely to be damaged. The Norton No 1 Team, captained by Mr. A. Lovatt, descended the pit. They were told to make a survey of the pit bottom, stables etc. and to come up in one hour. This they did and the captain made a detailed report of the conditions below. His report, was excellent, and deserved credit for his ready grasp of the essential facts and conditions. His concise and clear report of the chaotic state was remarkable when it was remembered that he and his men were breathing artificially in an absolutely deadly atmosphere, and frequently meeting fresh dangers and difficulties, most of the time being knee deep in water.

This report enabled the officials to determine the origin of the explosion, which, having begun in the Cockshead Seam. This seam was reached by a dip of 1 in 3 and about 800 yards in length. It was certain that a fire was burning in one of the goafs of this seam, and it was decided to close the pit for a few days.

The shafts were entirely covered over and sealed with sand, the only entrances into the shafts were a few small tubes fitted with plugs, which were fixed in for the purpose of taking samples of air, temperature and pressure of air.

A week later, most of the rescue brigades in the district were summoned, and the recovery of the pit was commenced. The water was cleared out of the pit by fitting a syphon and causing it to run away down the Cockshead Dip. The pit bottom was put into temporary repair, so that the cage could be lowered to the bottom level. During these operations it is interesting to note that two of the rescue men accidentally fell over the head into the water, but keeping calm, they walked up the roadway and emerged higher up from the water, no worse from the experience, except, of course, for the soaking, which was, in those conditions, not particularly comfortable. The Cockshead being the district from which the danger was to be feared, it was decided to stop it off for the time being. This involved the erection of three block stoppings, 27 inches thick, at the top of the dip, one in the main intake, and one in each of the two returns. As the ground was very loose, it had to be excavated on the bottom, sides and top before the foundations, which were of concrete, were put in. It was work involving much heartbreaking labour, as all the carrying had to be done by men wearing the breathing apparatus, the atmosphere being lethal the whole time. Finally the stoppings, two of which were about 15 feet wide by 10 feet high, were faced with laths and plaster, and after a preliminary exploration by rescue men, the fan was again started and the Holly Lane and Hard Mine seams, which branched off a level which crossed the top of the Cockshead Dip, were ventilated without mishap. Men were then able to go down the pit without breathing apparatus, and permanent repairs were put in hand, and in a few weeks coal was being drawn from the Holly Lane and Hard Mine Seams.

Three teams, the Norton, Birchenwood, and Grange all belonging to Robert Heath and Sons, were retained for the difficult and dangerous task of reclaiming the Cockshead Seam.

It was decided that the only way to do this with absolute safety, was by building block stoppings at intervals of 100 to 200 yards, according to circumstances, opening the doors or stoppings between the roads, and by repeating this ventilation of the district in stages. When the level along which the fire was suspected to be reached, the intake and return were to be stopped off, and the air was to be turned into the rest of the district. The intake air-way, which was the main haulage road, was found to be very much damaged, but the returns had suffered little in comparison. It was found possible, by taking the rope through grease filled stuffing boxes in the stoppings, to use a trolley below the stoppings for the conveyance of material, but, even with this advantage, the work was of a very arduous, exacting and dangerous nature, and the rescue teams deserve all the credit it is possible to give them for the manner in which the work was carried out, and for their courage and endurance during such a trying time, as they were fully aware that they were working in an atmosphere to which one minutes exposure through carelessness or failure of their apparatus would mean death. At the same time, we must give credit to the apparatus, which never failed in a single instance during the six months trial.

When the recovery was completed, in August, it ranked as the world's record for similar Work.

9. The Jamage Pit Disaster

Thursday 23rd November 1911 some coal appeared to be getting hot and it was partly loaded and sent up the pit. On Friday the manager discovered a trace of 'Gob Stink' which indicated to him that there was evidence of a gob fire. Although there was no fire to be seen he had the good sense to shut off the district by having a dam built. This was being done and at 9.30 am on Saturday 25th. November, an explosion took place and it blew out the nearly completed dams. Six men died with the effects of the afterdamp and six more were partially gassed. One having suffered a fractured leg and another badly burnt on his back.

All the men were got out of the mine within a few hours without the assistance of a mine rescue team.

A second more violent explosion took place at 6.30 on Saturday evening when fortunately no men were in the mine but sadly 27 pit ponies perished as nothing could have been done to save them.

Pathetic scenes were witnessed on the following Wednesday when the funeral took place of four of the men, they were:- Enoch Edwards, Frederick Lees, George Cork, and Harry Shaw. They were all from Bignall End and were highly respected in the community.

This was the second disaster at this pit. The other taking place on the 6th. July 1875, when five men died.

10. Some Events of the Strike of 1926

For the first time in British history, the industrial life came to a standstill. The railways, buses, trams all ceased to operate. Factories and mines closed and some 4,000,000 workers came out on strike on the 4th. May 1926 and a revolution had begun.

The flame was kindled in 1925, when the mine owners decided to reduce the miners' wages, and increase the working hours. The reason for this, they said, was that since 1921 the boom in coal exports had ended and that there was a depression in the manufacturing industries thus reducing the demand for coal. This seemed rather contradictory when the men were asked to work longer hours. This surely would have added to the surplus of coal. Even with the pittance the miners' received in wages for all the sweat and blood, the mine owners' claimed that most mines were working at a loss.

July 31st. 1925, known as 'Red Friday', the Government intervened, and Stanley Baldwin, who was then Prime Minister, agreed to provide a subsidy out of the taxes to maintain the wages for a period of nine months. A Royal commission was then set up to investigate the true state of the mining industry. Sir Herbert Samuel headed the commission and in March 1926, he recommended that the subsidy be withdrawn and the owners' claim for lower wages be accepted but rejecting the need for longer hours. The commissions findings were accepted by the Government and the owners, but was rejected by the Miners Federation, who took up the slogan, 'Not a minute on the day; not a penny off the pay'. The Miners' Federation now asked for help from the T.U.C. the Trades Union Congress, but they were not in favour of a general strike until the mine owners on the 13th. April went back on their word and demanded a wage cut ranging from 12 shillings (60p) to 15 shillings (75p) and an increase in the working day to begin on the 1st. May. This changed the minds of the T.U.C. and promised full support to the miners'.

On the 30th. April the Prime Minister sent the owners' offer to Herbert Smith who was President of the Miners Federation, who had already made the statement on wages as for longer hours he replied 'The present hours are long enough to supply all the coal for which a market can be found and are as long as men should be expected to pursue such a dangerous and arduous calling'

The T.U.C. on the 1st. May, told the Government that its members had voted unanimously for a general strike in favour of the miners' to begin on the 3rd. May. In the early hours of that morning, Baldwin stated: 'I had done all I could and there was no where else to go'.

And so it began on the 4th. May 1926, the full force of the strike was felt throughout the country. An unnatural silence fell because of the absence of public transport, the noise from factories, the streets and roads almost deserted of people as though an ogre was abroad and no one dared to venture out. In a few days however, the position changed and ugly violent scenes began to take place. The Army were brought in to keep essential services going, then men started to return to work, lorries were overturned, their loads scattered over the road. Trains being driven by amateurs causing some chaos and even death. Policemen and soldiers acting as guards on buses because the blackleg drivers were intimidated by the strikers. The 'Flying Scotsman' engine and four coaches were derailed at Cramlington, ten miles north of Newcastle. A length of rail had been removed, fortunately it was only travelling at 6 miles per hour as a precaution, because some volunteer platelayers had been attacked near there by striking railwaymen who had thrown stones at them. If the train had been travelling at its normal speed, there would have been a terrible disaster.

12th. May the Daily Newspapers came out bearing enormous headlines: GREAT STRIKE TERMINATED. The T.U.C. said that they had been given assurances that a settlement of the mining problem can be secured and this justified them in bringing the general strike to an end.

The miners' however, were not so fortunate, the mine owners proposals were sent to Herbert Smith via Mr. Baldwin. The Government offered to grant a subsidy of £3,000,000 but there was no improvement on the terms before the stoppage. The Miners' Federation refused and were determined to resist any cut in wage and an increase of their working day. The owners were adamant and refused to take them back unless they complied with their wishes. The Miners' had no alternative but to battle on alone, aware of the consequences that would ensue of great hardship, not only for them, but for their wives and children.

And so it came to pass for seven long months of deprivation and despair from which the mining industry never recovered. Some pits never reopened and men were left jobless. In 1927 there was in excess of 250,000 miners' without work. During the strike, other coal producing countries took advantage of the situation, and supplied our customers abroad and some of these markets were never recovered.

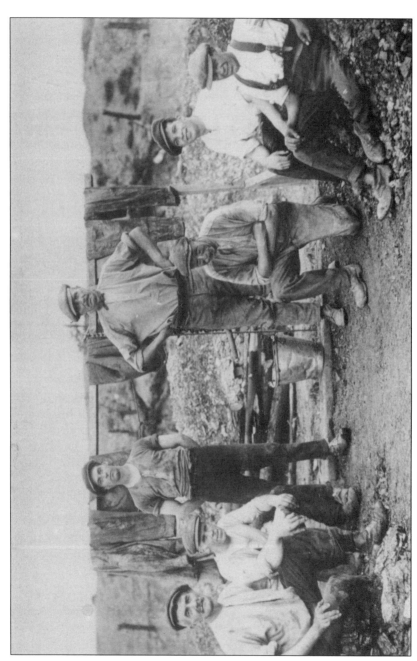

Outcrop miners in Cheadle, 1926

A few events that occurred in N. Staffs

- The relief committee at Wolstanton recommended the reduction of relief from 10 shillings per week for wives to 9 shillings and from 10 shillings per week for 1st. child to 3 shillings and 2 shillings for each subsequent child.

- At Newcastle the relief committee voted to stop the relief for the unemployed. 12 votes to 10 against, the reason for the boards decision was that they had an overdraft of £39,500 and would mean an extra three shillings and sixpence on the rates and the overdraft was to be paid off in 3 years. When the committee rose to go they were met on the steps of the building by a large crowd who shouted: 'Here comes the baby killers'.

- A crowd of about 300 mostly married with children marched to the workhouse at Chell and demanded admission because they were destitute.

- 200 children from Kidsgrove were fed and it was financed by Parkers Brewery of Burslem.

- Some 5000 miners' marched in an orderly procession through the streets of the Potteries singing, 'It's a long way to Tipperary'. It was a very hot day and some were overcome by the heat and hunger.

- Miners' were fined on several occasions for begging in the street.

- A young miner who was awakened by funny noises made by his father, and found that he had cut his throat. The son rushed to inform the police and, in the meantime his father had jumped through the bedroom window. He was taken to the infirmary in the mental institution and died the same day. The son giving evidence said, that his father was always in good health and spirits until the strike then he became depressed and complained of noises in his head that were driving him mad.

- The magistrates were kept very busy dealing with men arrested for coal picking off colliery tips and sidings.

Many miners' took the initiative in digging for coal in outcrops which at times were found lucrative because by this time coal was in short supply regardless of the large quantities being shipped from overseas. The Miners' Federation frowned on the practice of outcropping at first, but realised that it was the only way the men had to feed their families. In a very short time many outcroppers found they were better off financially than they were before the strike. There was of course the inevitable casualties caused by roof falls and even miniature explosions and fire caused by methane. Fights over territory and even a murder.

William Henry Phillips aged 51, left home to work in his outcrop. When he did not return at his usual time his neighbours formed a search party and discovered him in his outcrop buried by about 2 tons of dirt.

William Legge aged 27, of Denbigh Street, Hanley, accompanied by his mate, Edmund Mellor, went to work at their outcrop in the marlhole off Brook Street, now Century Street. The crut, in the face of the marlhole, was 2 feet 6 inches high and about 66 feet long. Not having much timber they found that the roof that day, was unsafe and decided to leave and get some timber. Mellor went out first, and Legge followed a few feet behind him. A large stone weighing over 2 tons crashed down on Legge completely burying him. Mellor seeing that he could not help him, got out and ran for assistance. Charles Leigh, a cousin of Legge, who had an outcrop near by, returned with Mellor to try and extricate Legge.

In the meantime a Doctor was sent for, and for some time the two men in very confined space and dangerous condition, managed to get Legge out and the Doctor pronounced that he was dead. There was quite a queer if not bizarre ending that this incident left in its wake. William Legge lived with his sister, and strange to say that the outcrop he worked in went under her house and she said that she could hear him hewing the coal when he was alive and, it was said, even after he had been Killed. Fact or fancy? We shall never know.

A tome could be written about the saga of the strike of '26, the deprivation and despair, and mans inhumanity to his fellow man. Lessons that should have been learned by that sacrifice but never have.

11. The Good Samaritans

A long time ago in 1926 A.D. This great nation of ours came to a standstill, and some 4,000,000 came out of work in sympathy with the miners' and a revolution began. Alas, after nine days the revolt ended, no shot had been fired and no one had been killed. The miners' however, were left to battle alone for seven long months of deprivation and despair. Never before had there been such a desperate struggle and finally a few weeks before Christmas, they lost the battle, a battle that they and their families, had fought and suffered so bravely. They had to accept lower wages and work longer hours. For some, there was no job to return to, because they had been blacklisted by the owners, and some pits had been allowed to flood and would never produce coal again. Jack Stevenson was one of these men. Jack and his wife Mary, had four children, their ages ranging from six to fifteen.

Jack sat in the humble living room of his house, which was almost bereft of furniture, with his head cradled in his hands. 'Ah dunna know wot wey're gooin'ter do Mary', he moaned. 'Well wot did thee say at pit this mornin'? Mary asked. 'Pit! Thee inna any pit no more', Jack replied lifting his head to answer her. 'The buggers', the owners, 'have let it flood anna thee' 'But wey, strikes o'er inna it'? Mary queried. 'Oh ah strikes o'er. Wot good it's done us. It's there wey ah serpose, ter sey bugger yer. Yer've managed o' this tarme wi' ite it, na see 'ow yer con manage when it inna theer any moor'. 'But anna thee cuttin' off the nose ter spite their face? It dunna make sense ter mey', Mary expounded. 'It dunna matter ter them woman. They con affode it. They've 'ad their pennorth ite of it. Thee dunna give a sod abite us do thee?' Jack replied with bitterness in his voice. 'Wot's ter become of us Jack? Wot about the kids, an' Christmas coming on?' Mary asked and, bringing her pinafore to her face started to sob. 'Ah dunna no Mary lass. Ah just dunna know'

Jack and Mary's eldest daughter, Ethel, was 15 years old and on leaving school, went into service as a scullery maid with a well to do family near Stafford. Ethel, during one of her days holiday had taken her youngest brother Ken, to see the big house where she worked. On that particular day, the Womens' Institute were holding a meeting with the lady of the house. When the meeting was over, the women departed to their own homes in the nearby village. Ethel was showing young Ken the Gardens when one of the women stopped and spoke to them. 'Good afternoon Ethel, and who may I ask, is this young gentleman with you?'.

'Good afternoon Missus Wilson. This is my youngest brother Kenneth. I've brought him to see the house and the garden. I thought a few hours in the country would do him good.' 'So it will my dear I am sure', and so saying, held out her hand to young Ken. 'I am very pleased to meet you young man.'

In all his six years Ken had never met such a lady and was rather taken aback at being spoken to like that, and being offered a hand in the bargain. He was shy and at a loss how to answer.

'Well lad have yer lost yer tongue'? Asked Ethel poking Ken in the side. 'Say Hello and please ter meet you Missus Wilson.' 'Ppleased ter meet yer missus', he replied shyly, looking up at her and then letting his gaze fall quickly to examine his black plimsolls 'I'm afraid 'e's a bit shy Missus Wilson.' 'How are things at home now Ethel, now that the strike is over?' 'Things are very bad ma'am. Dad's pit is flooded an 'e's still not working. I don't know 'ow they're goin' ter manage, they only get a bit of relief you see, and there's Christmas comin'. Me mam's at 'er wits end.' 'I am sorry my dear. How many are at home now? Asked Missus Wilson. 'There's me mam and dad, 'im 'ere and, me young sister and brother', replied Ethel. 'Tut tut', Mrs. Wilson remarked. 'Quite a lot of mouths to feed. You of course live in here, don't you'? 'Yes Ma'am' Mrs. Wilson stood deep in thought for a few moments looking intently at young Ken. She took a small note pad and pencil from her hand bag. 'I am going to see if I can do something for your family, I am not going to promise anything now but I will try. Will you give me your parents name and address?'

A few days later a letter arrived at the Stevensons. Jack opened it eagerly, and with some anticipation, for it was a rare occurrence for the Stevenson household to receive mail. 'Well wot does it see?' asked an impatient Mary. 'Oose it from?'

'It's from a Missus Wilson, 'er knows ah Ethel and it seems 'ers took a fancy to young Ken, an' would lark nowt better than 'ave ah young 'un fer Christmas' He passed the letter to Mary, "ere yo read it an tell us wot yo think'

'Well', said Mary after reading the letter, 'Er seems genuine enough and as 'er says 'ers got no kids of 'er own an' 'er would bey pleased ter 'ave 'im.'

'Well, wot d'yer think? Jack asked.

'Ee ah dunner no. Ah'd miss the lad. In any case would 'e goo?

"Ed be a young foo' if 'e did'na. Thee'll bey nowt 'ere for 'im.'

When young Ken came from school, Jack and Mary told him of the contents of the letter.

'Me'? he asked in surprise, 'Why me'?

"Ers took a fancy to thee lad that's wey', said Jack. 'It's an offer they cos'na refuse lad. Just think on it. Livin' in a posh 'ouse wi' thee own toys, better than 'ere cos ah conna give they or any on yer owt fer Christmas. Thee knows't that dust na?' Jack spoke the last few words with a tremor in his voice, his head bowed and his hands clenched showing the white in his knuckles.

Silence ensued for several moments and, young Ken realising his father's anguish, put his hand on his shoulder.

'It's alraight dad, ah'll goo if yer want me too'

Jack looked at his young son and smiled. 'Good lad. It wunna bey fer long, and just think they't see just 'ow the other 'alf live, a bit different than this poverty stricken place ah can tell thee lad'.

A week before Christmas, on Ethel's day off, young Ken made his departure hand in hand with his sister. They turned to wave good bye to their parents when they reached the corner of the street. Jack and Mary were standing on the doorstep waving in return.

It was a large house in its own grounds. Ethel with Ken in tow, walked up the gravel drive to the front door and rang the bell. The door opened revealing a beaming Missus Wilson.

'Welcome to my house Kenneth. I am so very pleased that you accepted my invitation. Do please come in'

They entered the hall which seemed, to young Ken, larger than the whole of his parents house. He started in amazement at the fine furniture and the large staircase.

Young Ken was shown a bedroom that was to be his own, and was left alone to unpack his meagre clothing which he had brought in a brown paper parcel. How fine everything looked to him who had shared a bedroom with three others, all in the same bed. The silence of the room was eerie except for the rustle of the trees outside and the bird song. How different he thought, to the environment he had been brought up in. But a feeling of loneliness seemed to tug at his heart and he felt terribly depressed to the point of crying.

Mister Wilson was a good humoured sort of man, balding and with fresh complexion, who took to Ken right from the start, trying his best to make him feel at home.

Christmas eve and the house started to take on a warm feeling with the waft of mince pies and other savoury odours that reminded one that Christmas was nigh.

'Well young Kenneth', remarked Mister Wilson looking over his paper

as they sat near the blazing log fire in the drawing room.
'It will soon be time for Santa Claus to pay you a visit.
I wonder what he will bring you eh?'
Ken smiled slightly and shrugged his shoulders.
'You do believe in Santa, do you?'
'I er, I don't know sir' Ken replied quietly.
His answer made Mister Wilson put down his paper and look at Ken
with some astonishment.
'Surely son, Santa must have visited you at home in Christmases past
and brought you toys, chocolates and other nice things?'
Queried the surprised Mister Wilson.
'No sir', said Ken.
'Did you not find some thing, er. . . or anything different on Christmas
morning? asked Mister Wilson.
'Oh that sir, yes there was always a stocking, me mam's stocking
hanging on the line over the fire'
'And what may I ask, did you find in the stocking, which I presume
Santa had left you'
'There were and orange an apple, some different nuts and sometimes a
block of chocolate or a selection box between us. Replied Ken smiling as
he remembered.
'And toys'? Mister Wilson asked eagerly for Ken to answer in the
affirmative. 'Santa did not forget to leave you some toys, surely not'.
Ken shook his head, 'I dunna think 'e ever come ter our 'ouse, cos ah
Bob, 'e 's me brother, towd me, me mam put those things in 'er owd
stockings'.
A pitiful look came over Mister Wilson countenance, and for several
moments did not speak only stared with some disbelief at the boy sitting
in front of him.
'Did you ever see Santa?'
'Yes, ah saw 'im last year when he came ter McIlroys up 'Anley', replied
Ken.
'And did you not speak to him an' leave him a letter to tell him what
toys you would like'?
A look of sorrow appeared on Ken's face.
'Ah did ner know that yer 'ad ter give 'im a letter, an' any road, me mam
said 'er could ner spare a tanner fer me ter go to 'im'.
'Oh I see', said Mister Wilson, 'It was sixpence to go into his grotto,
was it not?'
'Yes sir, d'yer think that's wey we did'ner get any toys'?

'Perhaps, perhaps', beamed Mister Wilson. 'But never you mind young Kenneth, Santa will be coming this year, I can assure you'.

'But 'ow can 'e sir? You said that yer 'ave ter send a letter, an' I anner sent one, ah did' ner know did ah?' Asked the bemused Ken.

'Ah, but you have lad'. Said Mister Wilson, his eyes gleaming with pleasure. 'I have sent one on your behalf. What do you say to that?'

Ken looked at his benevolent host and smiled shyly.

'Thank you sir', he said.

'Now Kenneth, off to bed with you. We don't want to keep him waiting do we'.

It took some time for young Ken to fall asleep, he was excited for what the morrow may have in store for him. He was aroused from his sleep sometime later, and he could have sworn that he felt a weight on his legs and in the moon light that lit the room, he saw a figure dressed in red, walking quietly across the room. This was a new experience for him, that at first made him afraid of this hooded figure, and he pulled the bed clothes over his head, then a feeling of exhilaration, that it could be no other but Santa Claus. He lay like this for some time hardly daring to breathe, then fell asleep.

He awoke next morning, Christmas day, and it was daylight. The first thing he saw was the large parcel on his legs and at the bottom of the bed a pillow, bulbous, and misshapen. Wild eyed with excitement, he jumped out of bed and carefully took the coloured wrapping paper off the parcel to reveal a box containing the largest train set he had ever seen. Hardly able to contain his joy and excitement he then examined the pillow case. This too was full of all types of toys and games. Then stepping backwards the expression on his face changed and he started to cry,

'What ever is the matter Kenneth?' Asked Mister Wilson, who, with his wife had now entered the room. 'Why are you crying'? Young Ken ran towards them and embraced Missus Wilson.

'Now, now lad, don't cry, you should be happy'

Kenneth lifted his tearful face and looked at her.

'I, I am, I am,' he sobbed. 'I was thinking of me sister's and' brother, and' me mam an' dad. They, they wunner 'ave owt, will thee, an' ah've 'ad o'these. It inna fair!'

The Wilson's looked at each other and smiled. Mister Wilson bent on one knee and pulled young Ken to him.

'What would you say if I told you that all your family are coming here to spend Christmas with us'?

"Ow, 'Ow con thee?' he asked, his eyes opening wide and looking into the kind face of Mister Wilson.

'Remember when I sent your letter to Santa', he said smiling.

Ken nodded, sniffed and wiped the tears from his eyes with the back of his hand.

'Well, I also sent a letter to your parents inviting them here for Christmas, and guess what?'

Ken shook his head and started to smile.

'They have accepted and, this very morning, I have sent a car to fetch them. What do you say to that?

Kenneth put his arms around Mister Wilson. 'Thank you sir, an' you Missus Wilson, you're the mostest kindest people in th' world.'

'Happy Christmas son', said Mister Wilson.

'A merry Christmas Kenneth' Added Missus Wilson.

12. Explosion at Holditch Colliery

Holditch Colliery known locally as Brymbo, was situated about two miles North west of Newcastle-under-Lyme.

There were two shafts, No. 1 was sunk in 1916 and No. 2 in 1912. They were approximately 2000 feet deep to the stone drifts from which the two seams, the Great Row and the Four feet were worked.

On the morning of the 2nd. July 1937, two men, Herman Payne and William Beardmore were working a coal cutter, and after it had cut about two yards, there was a fall of coal on the compressed air hose. The two men cleared the fall and the cutting started again. At a quarter to six the machine had cut past the gate end, and the back end of the cutter was about three yards past the left hand gate side pack, when Beardmore, who was ridding the cuttings, saw a flame which seemed to run round the picks then under the cut coal. It then went along the holing to where the cutting had started a distance of about seven yards. It came out of the cut and spread up the coal face towards the roof. In Beardsmore's words 'Like a wall of fire'. The two men, quite rightly, thought it best to get away from it as soon as possible, such was the intensity of the flame and the heat.

About this time there were some 55 miners' working on the face or near to, including two firemen, Jesse Moore and Earnest Astles and the overman, Trevor Hughes. The two firemen were quite close to the cutter. Moore being just on the return side of it and Astles at the rip in the Main Dip where he was preparing to fire a shot. The Overman, Hughes, was at the top end of the face near to the end of the left hand carving. Payne and Beardmore, the coal cutters, with others working on the face on the intake side of the machine, withdrew into the Main Dip. Those working further down the face were warned and they withdrew by way of the Right Hand Carving. Moore, the fireman, walked up the face with the fouled air current to warn any men to withdraw. But they had already gone being told previously by the Overman who had taken steps to get the men from the upper end of the face. But two men, W. Haystead and A. Stanton, who were working on building a pack in the middle waste between the Back Dip and the Left Hand Carving, failed to come out and by the time they realised the danger they were in, tried to get out but by this time the smoke was so dense they lost their way and wandered into another waste and were overcome.

By 6.15 am all the men with the exception of Haystead and Stanton, gathered at the bottom connecting cross cut at the entrance of the face and here, made plans to try and put out the fire. Several were ordered to carry bags of stone dust down the Main Dip to the face, whilst the Firemen and Overman went to investigate. The discovered that the fire had taken a good hold that the timber on the face was blazing and had started to crack, the roof was threatening to collapse. I was impossible to get near to the fire because of the heat so the overman ordered the stone dust to be dumped and spread about the fire as near as possible. Their efforts were futile and another retreat was made and a roll call taken. It was then at this time, that the two packers', Haystead and Stanton were found to be absent and efforts were made to try and find them. The would be rescuers tried to explore the Left hand Carving and the back dip. These were the only available means of access to the face but they encountered smoke and fumes of such intensity that it was impossible to continue and the search was abandoned with little hope it seemed that the two men would be still alive.

Meanwhile, the day shift officials for the Great Row and the Four Feet seam having been notified of the fire, arrived in the district and H. Bentley a Fireman from Great Row who was a stranger in the Four Feet workings, thought that some of the searchers had gone into the Right Hand Carving asked a night shift ripper, J. Hassell to show him there. Whilst they were there, the time now about 6.50 am an explosion occurred and seemed to confine itself to the coal face because no one was injured by it. They were on the edge of the blast. Bentley had his hair singed and with some difficulty found his way out to the Main Dip, where he learned that Hassell had not come out. Bentley though burnt, went back along the roadway with a collier, E. Beech who he had met in the main dip to try and find Hassell but the search proved to be in vain.

The effects of the explosion were felt at the bottom of the upcast shaft. Mr. Davies the manager and Mr. Whitfield the assistant manager had just arrived there. On learning that except for Haystead and Stanton, the rest of the party were safe. The manager, Mr. Davies, told them to withdraw.

Three more explosions were felt when the nightshift men were coming out. It was assumed at this time that there was no one else in the Four Feet seam except the two missing men. In the Main Crut, near 5's cross cut they met Mr. Davies and Mr. Whitfield, and they informed them that there had been four explosions and that a third man was missing.

The atmosphere in the return airway at 5's cross cut was examined and after consultation with his officials, the manager decided stoppings should be erected in the cruts just below the 5's cross cut, and he gave orders that sand, stone dust and building materials etc. be brought as quickly as

Holditch Colliery, 1951

possible. The decision was not an easy one to make to seal off the district knowing that three men were missing. If they were not dead now he would certainly have condemned them. He was however, convinced in his own mind and that of his officials, that the devastation of four explosions and the atmosphere prevalent at that time and to save further loss of life and devastation, his decision was the only thing to do. Whilst the material was being collected, probably to salve his conscience, Mr. Davies, accompanied by the assistant manager, two overmen and four firemen, went on into the Four Feet to make an examination. On their way down the Main Crut they felt a reversal of air indicating another explosion, the fifth. some of the party stayed behind here to detach some tubs from the rope, the rest went on to inspect the Right Hand Carving. Fifty yards or so further on they found firedamp in explosive quantity, and the party withdrew. There was still no signs of the missing third man, Hassell, although the searchers had gone further inbye than the place where it was said by Bentley where he would have been when the first explosion occurred at about 6.50 am. Returning form the Right Hand Carving the time now about 7.30 am they met Mr. John Cocks, the Managing Director who had just reached the bottom of the Main Dip. Mr. Davies, told him what had been done and how far he and his party had been. Mr. Cocks, with others, proceeded down the Main Dip nearly to the face. The ventilation doors were found to be open, probably due to the explosion. It was decided to leave them open because of the fire damp known to be present in the Right Hand Carving finding its way to the fire. The ripping near to the face had fallen. No fire could be seen and inflammable gas could not be detected. It was remarkable that there was no fire damp at this time because nearly all the intake air was now coming along this road. It was possible because of the fall of roof at the face, and the main road ripping that the flames had been smothered.

There was disagreement between Cocks and Davies about the stoppings that Davies had ordered to be done in the cruts just below the 5's Cross cut. Cocks, in spite of the disagreement, decided to put the stoppings in the roads of the Four Feet seam, one in the short length of about 10 yards of road in the Main Dip between the new narrow heading and the Right Hand Carving, one in the Back Dip inbye of the bottom cross cut and a third at the entrance to the Left Hand Carving.

This was a vital matter changing the original plan of the manager, resulting as it did, in the large death Toll. Mr. Cocks ordered the Holditch Rescue Team who had now arrived in the district, to make an inspection in the Right Hand Carving where the previous search had been made. The rescue team made their way right up to the ripping where they could not make any further progress because it had fallen and their way was blocked. They found no trace of Hassell the missing man. They were then sent to explore the Back Dip between the bottom cross cut and the coal face, hoping that they may come across Haystead and Stanton. Without a life line they found, due to the density of the smoke that it was impossible to continue. A lifeline was sent for, but meanwhile Mr. Cocks ordered the team to explore the Back Dip above the bottom cross cut to see if Haystead and Stanton had by chance, gone that way.

About 9 am two of H.M. inspectors of mines arrived and met Mr. Davies who was now in the pit bottom who told them what had happened and Mr. Cocks intention about the stoppings. When they arrived at 5's cross cut, a sixth explosion occurred.

Materials and men were arriving, fitters and electricians had gone down to disconnect pipes and cables and at about 10 am there were 28 men in the seam which included five members of a standby rescue team, the two inspectors and Mr. Cocks and four others on the haulage road inbye of the 5's cross cut. The Holditch Rescue Team were well on the way up the Back Crut. Just before 10 am there was another explosion, a small one followed by a larger one, the force of this blew the men off their feet at the pit bottom and reversed the ventilating system between the shafts and the Four Feet workings.

All the men in the seam were extensively burned, nine were brought up alive.

A total of 30 men lost their lives. Two by the fumes of the fire at 5.45 am One by the explosion at 6.50 am and 27 by the explosion at 10 am

A lot of questions were asked at the enquiry, mainly why the order by Mr Davies the manager regarding the positioning of the stoppings was countermanded by Mr. Cocks the Managing Director. The outcome of his decision was, we shall never know, the reason for the heavy loss of life.

Rescue

The Holditch Rescue Brigade was led by Azaria (Ezra) Clarke, Overman at the colliery.

The call for rescue was made at 6.30 am Two members of the team were already there having been on the night shift. One was on sick leave. Three others were summoned, one of them lived some distance from the pit. Four of the team descended the pit at 7.30 am.

They explored the Right Hand Carving to the rip which stopped their progress because of the fall. About this time the man who was on sick leave joined them. They then attempted to go down the Back Dip but experienced great difficulties because of the density of the smoke. Some time later they made their way up the Back Dip from the Bottom Cross Cut. They groped and stumbled about on the steep gradient through the black smoke and some time later the smoke grew less dense. At 10.10 am a massive explosion occurred. They were subjected to the force of the initial blast and then the backlash of the air but fortunately were not injured and were able to proceed through 5's cross cut to the Main Crut. Here they heard the telephone ringing. The atmosphere was foul and very dusty but after a few minutes it cleared. Azariah Clarke answered the telephone and the manager speaking from the pit bottom asked him for information. The manager then suggested that the team go back down the dip to explore. Clarke told him that this was impossible at that moment because the apparatus they were using was nearing exhaustion. The Brigade then returned to the pit bottom and exchanged the apparatus with another Brigade that was standing by. They then made their way inbye and on their way found an injured fireman, Bentley, and another fireman, Bloor, who was slightly injured. Obtaining stretchers they were carried out.

Arriving at the steep part of the Main Crut, they could see a fire blazing at the bottom. The explosion had burst a waterpipe the Brigade then subdued the flames which were coming from burning props and a cable. Some few yards further on they came across a number of injured men and gave them first aid and made them as comfortable as possible. One of the brigade was sent back to report to the manager and how many stretchers they required. They played a prominent part in evacuating the dead and injured among whom were some of their own colleagues. By this time it was about 4 pm They then made a final examination of the workings that were accessible. Having ascertained that there were no living miners' left behind and having noted the positions of the dead, they were ordered to withdraw as those in charge expressed fears that there may be another explosion at any moment.

There were some doubts as to whether there was still anyone left alive and at about 6 pm the brigade decided to descend the pit to make a further exploration. After an extensive search in very dangerous explosive conditions, The captain, Azariah Clarke, confirmed that no one would still be alive. He reported that the fire was still burning and, in his opinion, was worse when they had left the pit previously at 4 pm. The story of the rescue is full of heroism, and in the best traditions of the mining industry. 'Greater Love hath no man than this, that a man lay down his life for his friends'

List of Killed

Name	Age	Occupation
H.L. Adkins	35	Under Manager
J.L. Bloor	51	H.M. Sub Inspector of Mines
J. Cocks	57	Managing Director
P. Condliffe	35	Collier
J. Cooke	37	Collier
A.L. Cooper	30	Collier
A.E. Cornes	26	Haulage hand
H.J. Finney	41	H.M. Senior Inspector of Mines
J.W. Forrester	40	Hanley Rescue Brigade
T. Harris	46	Hanley Rescue Brigade
J. Harvey	39	Fireman
J. Hassell	35	Ripper
W. Haystead	45	Packer
W.S. Hodkinson	38	Underground Fitter
W. Hough	37	Hanley Rescue Brigade
F.J. Howle	36	Holditch Rescue Brigade
R. Jackson	35	Collier
H. Johnston	34	Overman
E. Jones	51	Fireman
T.H. Jones	28	Collier
S. Latham	28	Hanley Rescue Brigade
A. Mayer	39	Underground Fitter
H. Mitchell	44	Underground Fitter
W. Pepper	39	Fireman
G.T. Pickerill	30	Ripper
C. Price	33	Collier
G.T. Rushton	41	Ripper
A.W. Seaton	26	Collier
A.R. Stanton	31	Packer
F. Turner	22	Underground Electrician

Injured

Name	Age	Occupation
H. Bentley	47	Fireman
H. Birchall	34	Collier
P. Bloor	49	Fireman
J.O. Davies	45	Manager
G. Edwards	29	Collier
J. Lightfoot	33	Collier
F.C. Salt	39	Collier
G. Stanier	37	Collier

Holditch Colliery, 1951

13. The Haunting at Paddy's Crut

It was young Jimmy's first day in the pit. He was filled with mixed feelings of adventure and apprehension.

He had heard so much about the pit, from his two brothers and his father and his father before him had worked there. Bill, one of his brothers took him to the Overman at the pit bottom to ask him where he wanted him to work.

Heslop Rake, the overman was a Geordie, a large brusque man and he looked down at Jim sizing him up for the job he had in mind. 'This is me brother heslop, Weer d'yer want 'im ter goo?' asked Bill.

Heslop took the oil lamp off Jimmy, held it up, then proceeded to blow on the glass, he handed it back then did the same to Bill's lamp.

Heslop's gaze returned to Jimmy, stooping a little as though to get a closer look.

'Yer'd better tak 'im to Paddy's Crut me bonny lad to do some waggonin' fer Tommy Joones. Yer'd better 'ave a werd wi' Tommy an' tell 'im that ah've sent 'im. Then spend 'alf an oor wi 'im an show the lad wot te do, Billy lad'.

Jimmy and Billy made their way inbye with Billy explaining the Why's and where fors of the haulage system and the different headings they passed on the way.

'This is Haley's Dip and goes down ter get Great Row Coal.' said Bill as they passed a heading where some youths were pushing some tubs along its level. 'It's named after thee faither thee knowst'

'It inna is it'? asked Jimmy with a look of surprise.

'Wey is it named after me faither?'

'Cus thee faither was in charge o' making the crut an was butty on th' face.

'Crikey!' exclaimed Jimmy, 'Ah did'na know me faither were famous'.

'Ah nearly o' the faces dine 'ere ah named after the men that worked on 'em. Lark the place they't gooin' to na, it were code after a bloke named Paddy'

'Ah thote yer said ah were ter work wi' Tummy Jones'? asked Jimmy.

'Ah yer ah. Tummy werks theer na, eh's in charge o' that yeddin'' replied Bill.

Silence ensued for several moments. Jimmy having a bemused expression on his face.

'If it's code Paddy's crut, wey inna Paddy workin' theer an bey in charge instead o' Tummy Jones?

'Eh'd 'ave a job wunner 'e?

'Wey?', asked Jimmy.

'Cus eh's djed inna 'e', replied Bill smiling.

'Djed!'

'Ah'

'Wen?'

'Abite twelve month agoo last New years dee.' Bill paused as they were about to walk up a steep incline.

'This is code Wet Jig' he said at last. 'It's code a jig cus thee use full loads ter pull empties up an' thee control it bey a jig wale at the top. An' thee co it wet because o' the wayter'.

'Ah sey', said Jimmy, 'But 'ow did Paddy die?'

'By a fo' a dirt, eh were buried'

'In Paddy's Crut'? asked Jimmy.

'Ah, we'er they't gooin'. Eh were buried an' thee didna find 'im till next dee'.

'Wey' asked Jimmy

'Cus beyin' New Years dee, nowbody works dine the'pit on New years dee as thee knowst, it's bad luck.'

'Wey? Jimmy enquired.

'Ah dunner know do ah? It's sort o' trad. . . er wot's it, some it 'appened years agoo, a disaster ah think. Any road up, thee faither an' us never goo do we?'

'Well wey did Paddy goo'?

'Ee ah dunna know abite they young un, they wants ter know abite th' inside and th' ite side of a cats backsdie they dust. . . . Watch thee yed ere, roofs low, weights come on a bit' It was too late Jimy was so engrossed about the death of Paddy, that he walked into the twisted girder.

'Ouch'! He exclaimed stooping and rubbing his head. 'That 'urt that did'.

'Ah towd thee did na eh?' replied Bill. 'They't 'ave ter keep thee eyes open an'thee wits abite thee dine 'ere or they't end up lark Paddy they wut'.

By this time they had reached the top of the Jig and Bill paused to tell Jimmy about the workings of the large pulley that was situated in the middle of the road way. They walked in silence for about another five minutes when they came to the crut.

"Ere thee at, Paddy's Crut' said Bill.

'Wot dist see 'appened ter Paddy? asked Jimmy.

"E were buried by a fo', ah towd thee'
'But wot ah conna understand is, wey was 'e on 'is own?' enquired Jimmy.
'Ah that were a bit o' a mystery. 'E should na bin dine theer on his own, but some'ow er other 'e went dine that's wey 'e wanna funt till the next dee. That's way thee say 'e's 'auntin' the place'
'Auntin' the place! Dust mean 'is ghost? Jimmy's eyes were now protruding from their sockets like organ stops.
'Ah so thee see', replied Bill.
'Ast, ast they sane 'is er..'is er ghost ah youth?' asked Jimmy his voice now filled with apprehension.
'Na, ah an ah, but the some dine 'ere see thee 'ave'. 'Wee're was it thee funt 'im? asked a subdued Jimmy.
'Aif wee up th' crut these a landin' that leads ter th' air rood. Thee funt 'im in theer, an' wen thee got the dirt off 'im 'is yed were cut clean off.'
'Wot, is yed cut off?'
'Ah, cut clean off is yed were.'
He looked at his young brother who was now staring at him with his mouth wide open.
'Tht's wee thee see it's 'aunted. Paddy's walkin' abite wi' no yed on luckin' fer it'.
'Crikey'! Exclaimed Jimmy. 'Ah 'ope ah dunner say 'im!'
'If thee asks mey' Billy replied philosophically, 'it's a load a rubbish. Wen a blokes djed 'eh's djed, that's wot ah says any road up'.
They both stood in a pensive mood, Jimmy still with mouth agape and eyes sticking out like organ stops. Bill no doubt thinking of what he had just said.
'Wot's up wi' you' two, dunner yo' want work ter dee or wot?'
The two brothers, startled by the angry voice, looked quickly from whence it came. They perceived a short distance away the light of two lamps, and the dark shadow silhouetted behind them.
'It's Spider Gilson the fireman', whispered Bill. 'They't 'ave ter watch 'im, eh's a bully wi' lads'.
Spider Gilson was now alongside the two lads, he was a tall thin man and it was obvious why he had been nicknamed Spider. His legs were extremely long giving an impression that his torso was short and out of proportion to the rest of him.
'Oh it's they is it Billy Haley? he said with sarcasm in his voice. 'An' oose this with thee?'
'It's ah youth, young Jimmy'. Billy replied. 'Eh's started ter dee, an'

'eslop's towd mey ter tak 'im ter werk in Paddy's Crut waggoning fer Tummy Jones'.

A supercilious grin appeared on Spider's face.' 'Not another of the' 'aley's brood? Pit'll be full on yer just na, then wey con co' it 'aley's conner we'. The grin turned into a guffaw, Spider amused by his sarcastic remark. It was obvious that no love was lost between him and the lads' family, his father had had many altercations with Spider in the past, some very nearly to blows. Spider always saving himself from a thrashing by turning the other cheek at the last moment and threatening, on his retreat, Jimmy's father, with the sack. Spider, in spite, always reported the disputes to the manager, who, knowing the mens dislike of him, treated him with the contempt he deserved. Spider's face soon changed from amusement to a sneer. 'Dunner stand theer lark chips, tak 'im up the crut an' show 'im wot ter do an they get on wi'thee own job', he snarled and at the same time prodding Billy with his stick. Spider turned and soon disappeared into the darkness.

"e's a sod 'e is, woss bloke in th' pit, nowbody larks 'im' said Billy, 'One o' thase dees somebody's gooin' ter clobber 'im. Raight ah youth, yer sey thase tubs, well ah put thase 'ere off th' main road an wen thee brings the full loads dine, leave 'em 'ere and ah'll deal wi' em. Ast got me?

'Ah ah sey', replied Jimmy.

'Raight. Ah'll push up the fost tub an' they cost foller wi' th' other one. Na a word o' warnin'. Keep thee hands in th' middle an thee yed dine, cos the roofs low an' if the does na theyt lose thee fingers an thee yed. Ast got mey? 'ook thee lamp on thee belt betwain thee legs'

Bill took the first tub and started to push it along the crut his hands in the middle of the tub and his head pushing on his forearms. Jimmy watched his brother then proceeded to do the same.

Some 50 or so yards into the crut Billy stopped.

'This is the air road ah were tellin' yer abite. Behind that door they't find some posts that they't ave ter fetch when Tummy asks thee. Theer six foot posts and 'eavy so theet 'ave ter snigger 'em ah'll show thee wot ter do wen waive tuk thase up'. Another 100 yards of pushing they reached the stall. One youth about 20 years of age was loading coal into a tub the other man was half lying hewing a cut into the gleaming black coal. Billy overturned his tub, then went to Jimmy.

'Raight young un, let's sey 'ow strong thee at. Turn thee tub o'er lark wot 'ave just done. Wey 'ave ter turn 'em o'er so that wey con get the full tub ite, dost sey?'

Jimmy nodded and attempted like his brother, to overturn the tub. He

The top of the jig

strained until his face went purple, he felt the tub being raised but could not, how hard he tried, completely overturn it.

'Goo on Jimmy they cost do it'! urged Billy 'ave another goo' Jack Prosser the loader, stopped in his task and Tummy Jones the collier, stood up and watched the stripling wrestling with the tub as though with a Sumo.

'Goo on lad', urged Tummy Jones.

'Goo on, tip it o'er', shouted Jack the loader.

"E'll do it, 'e's strong as a little 'oss. Goo on ah youth'. Shouted Billy.

Jimmy not to be outdone, or let his brother down, gritted his teeth, took a deep breath and on his third attempt turned the tub on its side. he stood up his face beaming with pride.

'Good lad', said Tummy Jones.

'Ah good lad', laughed Jack the loader.

'Ah knew thee cud'st do it ah youth.' said Billy with pride.

'This load is ready ter goo Billy, an befer thee goost show yo'er youth weer the timber 's kept in th' air rood, wey want another post.'

Between them they pushed the loaded tub along the crut to the main road.

'Now ah'll goo an' show thee we'er ter get the post from the air rood, then ah'll 'ave ter leave thee' said Billy They reached the air road, and with a little difficulty because of the air pressure, they opened the stout wooden door. 'Make sure that they alweys keeps the dooer shut else they't interfere wi' the ventilation o'er the pit'.

Billy then explained the reason why they had to have return air ways. He then took a dog collar from his pocket and put around his brother's neck.

"Ere they cost borrer mine ter deey but theyt 'ave ter get one fer thee sel'.'

He then tied a piece of wire around the timber prop passed it between Jimmy's legs and fastened to his belt then hung the lamp on the dog collar round his kneck. He opened the air door and told Jimmy to get on all fours and drag the post up the crut. Jimmy did and felt like a pit pony. He was now left to fend for himself. Pushing the empties in, overturning them and pushing the full ones out.

Snappin' time came and went, and tummy told Jimmy to snig another prop from the air road. Jimmy was not very happy about this, for several reasons, one was of course, the fear that he might see Paddy which he did not relish the thought of, being in there alone with him. The other reasons were the effort of opening the heavy wooden door and closing it. Would he able to open it when he wanted to come out, if not how long would it be before he was released, and lastly, being on all fours dragging the post up the crut. But never the less, it had to be done. The door in the entrance to the air road, did take all his strength to open as he knew it would, but eventually it did, sufficient enough for him to squeeze through.

The air road was about four feet high and about five feet wide. The roof was supported by wooden props at about eight feet intervals. The roof and sides were of a grey stone and the place took on an eeriness and the silence of a tomb. He looked around him furtively, the dim light of his oil lamp casting dark shadows from the roof supports. A terrific bang behind him as the door shut on its own because of the pressure of air, made him jump with fright and his lamp fell to the floor and he was left in total darkness. The blackness enveloped him, a blackness he had never felt before, even in the darkest night up above on the surface, and he started to panic making him disorient. He groped about frantically with his arms, tripping over the stones beneath his feet. If only he could find the air door, he thought. He would be able to open it and find his way somehow along the crut to a light and Tummy. His reasoning seemed to calm him, and after a few moments of respite, he tried, by feeling along the wall and timber supports hoping that he would soon come upon the air door. His progress was slow and painful and, after a while he realised that by this time he should have reached his goal and that he must have been travelling in the wrong direction. Jimmy, frightened and lost, slid to the floor and started to sob.

The silence, like a tomb overawed him, then broken by a sharp crack, then another as the timbers above him strained with the weight upon them. Jimmy endeavoured to make his eyes see through the blackness but to no avail. He sat now on his haunches his head buried in his arms, another crack, louder this time, above his head followed by a moan and a trickle of dirt showered his head and shoulders. He was reminded immediately of the saga of Paddy's ghost that his brother had related to him earlier. He closed his eyes tighter and buried his head deeper into his arms.

'If that's they Paddy, ah dunner want ter know. They cost bugger off they cost! Dost 'ear mey? They con bugger off!'

He was answered by a large creaking sound and another shower of dirt upon his head.

'Ah've towd thee anner ah? Ah dunner want ter know thee. So bugger off!'

How long he sat there, haunched, his head buried in his arms he did not know, but to Jimmy, alone and frightened, it seemed a lifetime. Suddenly there was a change of air, like the wind on a heath that made him shiver, then a voice, far off just audible.

'Jimmy, Jimmy'.

'Bugger off, Bugger off, ah've towd thee!' Jimmy shouted.

'Jimmy'. The voice or who ever it was was much louder now and nearer.

'Please', Jimmy implored, 'Wey dus'na look fer thee yed some weer else. Ah anna got it, bugger off an' leave us bey'!

He heard a noise close by then. . . a few moments later a hand gripped his shoulder. . . .'Jimmy' the voice said.

Startled by the hand that gripped his shoulder, he lifted his head and opened his eyes, horror stricken for what they might behold. There was now light in the darkness and a dark figure bending over him. 'Jim lad, ah were worried abite thee. Wot 'appened?'

Jimmy, his face now tear stained change from terror to one of relief. 'It's they. . . . It's they Tummy. Inna it'?

'Of course it's mey lad, oo dust think it were'? Tummy asked.

Jimmy got to his feet slowly, shook his head and started to look for his lamp.

'Ah 'eard a bang be'ind me and ah dropped me lamp an' were in the' dark an ah didna know which wee ter goo, so ah sat me sel dine an' weeted for yo ter come an' fetch me'

'But oo were that yer were tokin to?' asked Tummy

'Tokin too'? Asked Jimmy.

'Ah they were tokin ter somebody, ah 'eard thee' said Tummy.

Jimmy found his lamp, turned and looked at Tummy.

'It were 'im wanna it?'

"Im, 'im, oose 'im?' Queried Tummy.

"Im', replied Jimmy sheepishly. 'It were Paddy'.

'Paddy, Paddy oo?'

'They know'st. . . Paddy's ghost'.

A large smile appeared on Tummy's face.

'Did yer see 'im?'

'Na, ah did na, ah kept me eyes closed, ah were ter fraightened, but ah knew 'e were 'ere'.

"Ow?' asked Tummy his grin getting wider.

'Cus ah 'eard 'im groaning an' creakin' an' droppin' dirt dine me neck. 'E were lookin' fer 'is yed thee knowst'.

'Did Paddy speak ter thee?' asked Tummy.

"E did na at fost. Then ah 'eard 'im co me name, very quite it were as though 'e were a long wee off'

'And wot did yer see ter 'im?'

'Ah towd 'im ter bugger off, ah 'ad na got 'is yed, an' goo luk fer it some weer else'.

By this time, Tummy could not contain himself and he started to laugh.

'It's nowt ter laugh at Tummy, it were fraightening ah can tell thee!' exclaimed Jimmy.

'Ah dare see it were lad' Tummy said trying hard to control his mirth. 'Come on, let's get that lamp lit so wey con get some work done'.

The haunting of Paddy's Crut still remains an enigma. Tummy Jones in an effort to dispel Jimmy's fears, explained to him that the groaning and creaking noises he heard was the timber posts taking on the weight of the roof above, that can be heard when everything was quiet. This however, was not enough for young Jimmy, for he was adamant, that Paddy was there and looking for his head. The next day he asked Heslop the overman, to find him a job in another part of the pit.

14. Explosion at Mossfield March 1940

Mossfield Colliery, was situated on the outskirts of Longton and was known to all the miners' who worked there as 'Old Sal'. There were two shafts, both sunk to a depth of 440 yards. The explosion occurred on Thursday 21st. march 1940, shortly after 1 am on the nightshift, in the Cockshead seam.

There were 12 men including the fireman working there, 11 were killed and only the fireman survived.

On Friday the 15th. March, a contract collier, William Neil Washington, reached 15s level face at about 6.30 am The coal had been cut and was ready for loading. He noticed a smell coming from the waste pack, which he described as an oily smell. The day shift fireman, Marshall Carson, also noticed the smell when he was about 10 yards down the face, he followed the smell down to No 3 waste where he met Washington, who mentioned the smell to him. Carson then examined the face and satisfied himself that the smell was coming from the pack. He then came outbye and met the overman, John William Birks, and told him about the smell.

Birks examined the face, then the waste and, he too said that there was a bit of a smell. He got into the waste and he came to the conclusion that it was just the hussle that was causing the smell. Hussle is a very friable carbonaceous shale lying immediately above the coal seam. He gave orders to men on the face to get all the loose coal out of the waste. He went away and returned at 10.30 am where he met the undermanager.

'Have you been round the third waste, Sam?' he asked.

'Yes,' replied Sam Barker the undermanager.

'Can you perceive anything different about it?' Birks asked.

'It's about the same only a bit thicker', the undermanager replied. 'But any how we will go together and have a look at it'.

They both went into the waste as far as they thought it safe to go. Birks got down on his knees, smelling at the loose stuff that had fallen, but he could not smell anything. He dusted his trousers and detected dust coming out.

'Well, Sam, there's wind coming through here'.

The undermanager agreed with him.

'It looks to me that we will have to stop this up some way or another', said Birks.

Samuel Barker, the undermanager, took action immediately, and gave Birks orders to get the men to timber the waste in order to make it safe for building a stopping in front of the debris, through which the wind was coming. Barker then went outbye and met the manager, Joseph Foster, at the pit bottom. He told him what he had found and what he had told Birks to do. Barker, the manager went to see for himself. When he arrived there at about 1 pm the timbering had been completed and he agreed with Birks, that the best thing was to put in a stopping, and gave instructions for the work to be done, and at the same time he gave orders for a second stopping to be built across the waste some few yards nearer the face. The work at this pack proceeded without intermittence during the weekend until it was completed on Tuesday, 19th. March.

But with all this, the picked workmen who were skilled in pack building, and the supervision by officials, the manager considered there was still a slight trace of smell when he arrived on Friday evening between 8 and 9 pm. Carson, the day fireman, thought there was a faint smell on Saturday morning. Arthur Seaton, the fireman on the night shift, who was injured and survived the explosion, made a statement whilst in hospital, that on the Friday night previous to the night of the explosion, that there was still a faint smell, and in his opinion, it was definitely gob-stink. He agreed however, that on the night shift, when the explosion occurred, there was no trace of the smell and he considered that the barrier pack had dealt effectively with the trouble.

On Wednesday, the 20th. March, work proceeded as normal throughout the day shift, the afternoon shift and so was the night shift, until at about 1.15 am on thursday morning when an explosion blasted the Cockshead seam.

There were, at that time, 12 men including the fireman, in and near the 15s. level face. Arthur Seaton the night fireman, the only survivor, related his experience.

'At that time, I had just come down the face to fetch some Cardox shells from the tub in the level, when I sensed something. Then there was a complete blackout. I thought that something had struck me and remembered nothing more until I regained my senses in hospital'.

Further outbye, a roadman, George Bolton, felt a peculiar sensation in the ears and then noticed a cloud of whitish dust coming towards him from inbye. He was quite sure, he said at the inquest, that he heard no noise and saw no flame. He telephoned the pit bottom, and spoke to Thomas Shenton, an overman, who was in charge of the traffic at the Pit Bottom and the main roads and also with Charles Clewlow, the fireman in 'H Level' district, a level on the opposite side of the main dip about 150 yards below 15s. level. Clewlow said that at 1.10 am, he had completed

Mossfield Colliery

his inspection of the level near the face, when there was a rush of wind and then a cloud of dust. He went to the face, and finding the men there were alright, he went outbye and telephoned Boulton who asked him 'To come quick to 15s.' He went at once and found Boulton. Clewlow then telephoned the Manager who told him to withdraw the men. This he did, then went inbye along 15s. level with Boulton and met Shenton. They were soon joined by other men and, with their help evacuated the dead and the injured.

15. The Leek Puddings

Most miners' in the Durham Coalfield had a burning ambition to beat their workmates at growing the best and largest leek. To many it became an obsession spending hours when not working in the pit, nurturing, guarding the precious vegetable as though they were babies. Indeed, their fanaticism in growing of this vegetable exceeded the loving care in some cases than shown to their own flesh and blood. Noxious brews were invented as fertilizers and the secret guarded almost to the point of death. Such was their devotion to grow them and to beat their workmates.

The climax to all the weeks of anxiety came when the annual leek show was held at the town halls, village halls or the working mens clubs.

An invasion of men from Durham to North Staffs started in the 1930's in the search for work and, later during the last Great War when some hundreds were transferred to more productive mines, to procure the much needed coal for the war effort. They brought with them their families, their traditions and of course, their expertise in growing the biggest and best leek in the world.

The annual leek show held in a working mens club in Newcastle, Staffs, that is, was crowded to capacity, the tables set out and groaning under the weight of the largest leeks ever grown. Valuable prizes and trophies were displayed awaiting for the judges to proclaim the winners.

The contestants were mostly Geordies' waiting with anticipation and anxious looks for the judges to assess their prodigy, which each and every one thought theirs was the supreme champion and could not be beaten. Although sly furtive looks at the next mans or even Jack's across the way may offer some stiff opposition. Tension mounted and a hush descended on the room as the connoisseur moved form table to table, halting momentarily now and then to inspect the produce and make notes on his writing pad.

Alf and Colin were mates and worked together at the Silverdale Pit. Their wives, Audrey and Doreen, were with them at the show. Doreen looked with envy in her eyes at the prizes awaiting to be won which, in her estimation, were marvellous and yearned for one to be hers.

'Ah dunner know wey yo' two dunner 'ave a goo at growin' leeks' she said, giving her spouse a nudge in the ribs with her elbow. 'Just look at them prizes. Ah could just do wi' them set o' saucepans and look at that clock, it would look very nice on ma mantle piece that would. Ee ah dunner know about you' two. D'you Doreen?'

'Thase two?' answered Doreen 'The only thing thase pair know that comes ite a th' grind is taters, oh ah an' coal o' course'. She started to giggle at her home grown philosophy. Alf turned to his wife a near angry look in his eyes. 'Luk Duck, if ah've towd yer once, ah've towd yer year after year wen wey come 'ere, thase blokes ah nearly o' Geordies, an' o they know abite is getting' coal, growing thase leeks an' drinkin' Newcastle Brown ale. Thee goo mad growin' thase, thee dunna give ah lads a luk in'.

'Ah,' said Colin not to be out done. 'Yo pair would soon start moanin' if wey were ite o' the tarme dine the' allotment lookin' after leeks. 'Avin' dees off from werk. Wunner yer eh? Thase buggers' 'have ter camp dine theer at this tarme o' the' year for fear o' somebody nobblin' them. Theer fanatics thase ah. Anna thee Alf?'

'Theer woss than fanatics thase ah. Thee wunner trust the own mother wen it comes ter growin' leeks,' answered Alf. Audrey turned and taking Doreen's arm in hers started to walk from the building.

'Com on Doreen let's goo wom. Thase pair ah beginnin' ter turn nasty. Yer've gotta watch wot yer see or else'. Alf and Colin followed behind them discreetly.

The following monday came and Alf and Colin were on the night shift. About 2 am and 'snappin' time. Colin was sitting on a chock piece which is a piece of wood used as a roof support and Alf was reclining against a tub.

'Ow did yo and your lady goo on at the wick end after wot was said on saterdee,'? asked Alf taking a bite from his bacon and cheese sandwich.

'Thee were 'ell ter plee' answered Colin. It's o'raight fer them ter goo on abite they an' mey growin' leeks. Wey're dine th' pit o' the tarme an' them two's sat at soddin' wom. Wey dunna they 'ave agoo at growin' th' soddin' things?' 'They't raight youth, Ma missus never spock ter mey o' dee sundee, 'er kept on abite them blasted saucepans and 'ow nice that clock would o' lucked on th' mantle piece,' said Alf taking a swig from his tin water bottle. He then envisaged Colin's missus with her brood of seven children and with one on the way. "Er anna got much time ter sit abite', he thought. 'If thee 'ad ter come dine this 'ole, lark us, Thee'd 'ave som'it ter moan abite,' he continued.

The sound of footsteps echoed in the silence then in the distance a lamp partly illuminated the darkness. The light came nearer and the dark silhouette behind it spoke: 'Are yes ave'n yer snap lads'? Colin and Alf recognised who is was because of the Geordie accent. It was Bob Thompson the district deputy. He was short and thickset and somewhat overweight and had come from Durham during the war years. He squatted beside Alf resting his back against the tub and seemed oblivious to the lumps of rock and coal under his backside. The two men noticed the rivulets of sweat making streaks down his coal blackened face.

'Ee lads ah'm just aboot boogered. I've just come up th' auld return dip from 5's and it's bloody 'ard gooin' ah can tell yer. Gis a drink of yer watter bonny lad ah'm dry as a bone'. Alf handed him the tin bottle. Bob took a short drink swilling the dust from his mouth and spat it out. He raised the bottle again to his mouth and started to gulp it avidly.. 'Owd on', shouted Alf snatching the bottle from him. 'That waiter's got ter last me o'naight'.

'Sorry lad a was that thirsty. Ah 'ad a bellyful o' Newcastle Broon on sundee neet. Ah keep seein' ter ma bonny lass at yem. Pet ah says, ah must cut me drinkin' down wen ah got go work next dey. She only laughs ye known an' says, aye an pigs might fly. But wot con yer do 'specially when yer mates won the best leek in th'show. Theer were drinks all round all saturdee neet an' same agen all day on sundee. Wę 'ad ter carry 'im yem in th' end carry in' that blasted leek in his arms like a bairn' Bob sighed, then laughed a little, shaking his head as he recalled the events of the weekend.

'Back down to business', he said at last. 'That return dip ah've joost coom up, there's a weight coom on an' the tops started ter coom doon. Ah need some men ter timber up an' keep the air rood clear. He looked intently at the two men. 'It's now good looking at us Bob, Col' and mey ah've got a dressin' o' coal ter shift yet. Any road up, the last tarme wey did extra werk fer they, wey did'na get peed fer it.'

Silence ensued for a few moments and Alf thought Bob might turn a little nasty and bring his official status into his request. After all Bob was the district deputy.

Alf took from his pocket a small silver coloured tin and opened it carefully, it's contents a brown powder-snuff. Alf knew that the deputy was addicted to snuff that is why he always carried the little box with him, a kind of sweetener when the deputy wanted some extra work doing, needless to say the two mates were not partial to the taking of snuff, a chew of tobacco yes, but not brown dust stuffed up your nostrils there was a enough black dust going up without adding to it.

'Try a pinch o' this youth, it's fresh ter naight', said Alf proffering the tin. Bob's nose twitched as the aroma of the snuff reached it. His eyes seemed to gleam in the light of their lamps and a flicker of a smile appeared on his countenance in anticipation of pleasure. He wiped his fingers on his trousers to clean them, and with the index finger and the thumb he pinched as much snuff they could possibly hold and proceeded to inhale it up his

"Ow did yo' and your lady goo on at the wick end?"

nostrils. He closed his eyes and a look of sheer joy came over his face.

'Crikey! exclaimed Alf inspecting the crater in the snuff which Bob's finger and thumb had made. 'Thee was nearly nowt left'.

Bob's eyes opened at last a beaming smile on his face.

'That was champion, bonny lad. Now wot aboot the air rood from 5's.'

'Ah reckon yer could get Bill Smith and his mate Spike ter do it in the next stall. Thee've drawn off theer'. Colin said. Bob contemplated the suggestion for a few seconds. 'Ah tell yer wot bonny lad. Gi's another pinch o' that snuff and ah'll think aboot it'.

Alf reluctantly took the small box from his pocket, tapped the lid a couple of times then unscrewed it. Bob's finger and thumb once again delved into the box taking another oversized pinch which he quickly and with some skill stuffed up his nostrils, then, to complete the procedure wiped his nose with the back of his hand. Bob relaxed and it seemed, all was well with the world.

Alf and Colin smiled at one another, the prospect of the unwanted job now disappearing, and began to quiz Bob on the result of the leek show.

'Who tuk fost prize then Bob?' asked Colin.

'Jacky 'utchinson, Geordie Jackson took second and guess who took third?' Bob replied beaming at the two mates.

'Not they! They dids'na dist?'

'Aye ah did, ah did that me bonny lad', Bob answered smiling and nodding his head.

'Ah conna sey wot good thee ah', said Alf. 'Surely yer conna eat 'em after yo've buggered abite with 'em. O that funny stuff yer put on 'em ter mak 'em grow, ah bet thee taste lark nowt on earth.'

Bob's back stiffened his eyes standing out like chapel hat pegs. Alf knew at that moment in time he had said the wrong thing, for after all the growing and eating leeks was sacrosanct to Geordies', a subject not to be taken lightly or a butt for joking.

'Wot doo yoo lot doon 'ere knoo aboot taste?' Retorted Bob angrily. 'What wi' yer oatcakes and lobby, if ye's con eat that lot ye's con eat owt!'

Alf and Colin were thinking that their beneficent gesture with the snuff was fast wearing off and at any moment they would be ordered to work in the return dip in 5's. Alf realised that quick and drastic action was needed to save face.

''Ere thee at Bob 'ave another pinch, tak the box'. He hurriedly took the box from his pocket and gave it to him.

Bob was very reluctant to accept the gift at first, but the temptation proved to much for him and he snatched the box, started at it for a few moments, then tapped it with his finger and unscrewed the lid and took another pinch. In a few moments his attitude changed and became more affable.

'Oor lass makes the best leek puddin' ever tasted', he said with pride if not boastfully.

'Ah, wot's she put in 'em?' asked Colin rather coyly and not wishing to arouse Bob's wrath again.

'Why ye dafty, leeks o' course and soom mince, pastry and soom oother stuff that oonly she knows aboot' He smacked his lips as he recalled the delicacy. 'Ambroosia, aye food fit fer the gods'.

The two colliers' looked at each other and smiled. There was a kind of telepathy between them and each knew what the other was thinking.

'They't making ah mouth water Bob. Dust think yo'er lady con make us some? We'd get 'er a barley wine next tarme 'er comes ter the club'. Alf said.

Bob did not answer for several moments. There was a thoughtful expression on his face. At last he rose painfully to his feet and looked down at the two mates.

'Aye. Ah can ask 'er'. With this he started to walk away. 'Yer'd better get that dressing o' cool in an' ah'll get Smithy and 'is mate ter do that job in 5's'. In a few moments he was gone, swallowed up in the darkness.

The following night Alf and Colin were busy putting up some timber to support the roof, when Bob appeared.

'Ah've spooken te our lass and she's agreed ter mak ye's a coople o' puddin's . But me pet says she wants a barley wine off each of ye's. An' yoo two can coont yersel's lucky. The bonny lass is usin' me prize leeks.

The rest of the week they hardly talked of anything else but the promised leek puddings. Their imagination soared thinking of the tasty morsels that by the week-end would be theirs. On Friday night shift, Bob informed them that the leek puddings had been made and he had left them in the deputy's office awaiting their collection when the shift was over.

They were both impatient for the shift to pass quickly, and Colin suggested that as soon as they had got them they would go to his house, which was the nearest, and devour them. Such was their impatience to partake in the tasting of as Bob had said,: 'Ambroosia, aye food fit fer the Gods'.

'Dunna talk daft. Owd thee 'osses. Wey've weeted this long, so ah see, let's weet till we goo fer a pint saterdee afternoon wen wey've 'ad a couple 'ours kip. Ah'll warm em up an' wey con enjoy em wi' a pint.' Alf said.

'Ah o'raight' replied Colin, 'It maks sense that does youth, wey'll enjoy 'em better as thee said'.

Colin sat in the public bar with a pint of mild in front of him, waiting impatiently for Alf. He watched the door of the bar with its frosted glass with the words PUBLIC BAR etched into it. At last Alf entered carrying a small oblong parcel, wrapped up in an Evening Sentinel. Colin all expectant, and mouth watering. Alf walked briskly to him his face impassive.

'They'st got 'em then?' asked Colin.

'Oh ah've got 'em', he replied and dropped the parcel on the table. Colin was a bit surprised at Alf's attitude, thinking by this time he would have been elated.

'Wot's up youth, Wot's wrong. Yo'er lady upset thee?'

'Ah'll tell thee wot's wrong, he replied angrily and at the same time unwrapping the parcel.

'Ah went in ter the office as Geordie said an' saw this parcel by the Barometer. Ah picked it up and wen ah got wom an' opened it ah funt this'. By this time the parcel had been unwrapped. Colin was looking at the contents in bewilderment.

'Wwot is it'? he stuttered in a hoarse voice he did not recognise as his own.

'Ah'll tell thee wot it inna.' Bawled Alf. It inna soddin' leek puddin's, it's four rinds of bacon an' soddin' egg. Ah must a picked up somebodies soddin' snappin'!'

16. Explosion at Sneyd Colliery

The explosion, the worst in the North Staffs Coal field for several decades, occurred on January 1st. 1942, and killed 57 men and boys. 55 died immediately and 2 others died in hospital from the injuries received.

It began at 7.50 am in the Banbury Jig by coal dust. The source of the ignition was disputed at the Board of Trade Inquiry, and the theory of Mr. John Hebblethwaite, the Manager as to the cause was: 'After thoroughly investigating and considering all possible causes of this explosion, I have come to the conclusion that six coal tubs were turned in at the top of the Banbury Crut Jig without any empty wagons being attached to the other end of the rope. From some unknown cause the load at the top of the jig ran away, and as these six loads careered down the jig, the upcoming rope possibly getting behind one of the wheels'. He was then questioned by the counsel and to clarify 'Getting behind one of the wheels'. The Manager replied 'Got to get over the front wheel between the wheel and the bottom of the tub and had become wedged' He went on: 'When this impact occurred at the pass-by it would be responsible for pulling the jig wheel out; and at the same time breaking the rope. If the tubs were not already derailed, this would derail them. A pair of glands covering a $\frac{1}{2}$ inch square hole in the compressed air main was knocked down the pipes a matter of $6\frac{1}{2}$ inches. The escape of compressed air at 80 lbs. per square inch pressure would increase the amount of turbulence already set up by the runaway tubs. Immediately following this, the tubs got rucked up and damaged the power cable. The preformed cloud of dust produced by the rucking of these tubs, due to the force that had been thrown int the jig, would travel back up the jig being assisted in doing so by the ventilation which was travelling at 200 feet a minute, and when it was almost gone, the finer particles, which were still in an agitated state, due to the turbulence of the compressed air, were, I feel sure, ignited by the following causes;- frictional sparks from the tubs crossing the compressed air main, and steel arches at the time when there was rucking up, and also from the sparks produced form the wheels and the breaking rope; electrostatics sparks from the discharged compressed air; spontaneous electrification of the dust cloud, I feel sure played some part in making the dust cloud easily ignited than in normal circumstances. The fourth possibility is that the cable, and I have gone into this very fully with people who know a lot more about cables than I do myself — was concerned, but I have come to the conclusion that the cable was not responsible'.

After a lot of debate, theories, Sir Henry Walker, who headed the inquiry, published his findings:-

1. That the up-going rope got over the inside wheel of the first tub of the set coming down at the time of the runaway.

2. That the marks between the strands of the sample rope examined were made by the rope rubbing against the front right hand corner of the first tub coming down, and that the flakes of mild steel found embedded in the rope came from the bottom of this tub.

3. That the capel of the up-going rope was caught against the sole of this tub, and so pulled off the jig wheel being pulled down and the set derailed at the same time.

4. That (3) occurred when the first tub of the down coming set was about 10 feet above the cock in the air main.

5. That, thereafter, the derailed tub or tubs displaced the cock and then damaged the electric cable.

And I think He went on:

(a) That the dust which was ignited was dust from the Jig and not from the runaway tubs.

(b) That such dust had been ignited before either the hole in the air main had been exposed, or the electric cable damaged;

(c) That the ignition of such dust was due to heat generated by friction between the up-going rope and the underside of the first down coming tub of the runaway set.

The Aftermath

Victims of the disaster ranged from boys of 16 and 17 years of age to veteran miners' who had worked in the No 4 pit for years.

The family circumstances of many of the victims gave poignant indication of the shadow which the disaster had thrown over many homes.

In one case, a wife lost her husband on their wedding anniversary — New years Day. Another lost her husband and her son.

Thomas Glibbons, aged 64, who at first they thought was the only survivor, owed his life to his intimate knowledge of the pit, having worked there for nearly 50 years. He was working near the pit bottom, driving a stationery compressed air engine hauling tubs from the Banbury seam. There was, he said, a tremendous blast of air which blew him off his feet,

Sneyd Colliery, 1950

and was hurled across the roadway and he lost consciousness. The next thing he remembered, was coming to and finding that he was in complete and total darkness, covered with dust. He found it difficult to breathe but he managed to crawl on his hands and knees off the main road of the Banbury Seam, into the return airway of the Holly Lane district. It was very narrow, and just big enough to allow a mans body to squeeze through. With his intimate knowledge of the workings even though in total darkness, he crawled about 200 yards where he met some men who worked in that seam, who had heard the explosion. They gave him a drink of water, and Thomas lost consciousness again, and the next thing he remembered was waking up in hospital. Ernest Stone, of Burslem, was in charge of the telephone communications underground near to the pit bottom. He was in a recessed position and so escaped the full blast of the explosion. He was the first to report the explosion to those above. Although suffering from shock, and in a dazed condition, he continued at his post for three hours until he developed dizziness and was made to leave the pit.

By the early afternoon eight rescue teams had been at work.
Three teams from Sneyd Colliery
Three " " Chatterley Whitfield Colliery
One " " Black Bull
One " " Hanley Deep Pit.

By the second of January, all hope was abandoned that any one else was alive in the Banbury Seam. Recovery work by the rescue teams and fresh air men proceeded. They encountered two large falls which had to be cleared before they reached the remainder of the missing men.

16 bodies had been recovered by this time. Heroic efforts were made by the rescue teams, headed by the manager, Mr. Hebblethwaite, to recover more had been in vain.

By Monday 5th: January, all but 5 bodies had been recovered. Mr. Cumberbatch, the Director and General Manager of Sneyd Colliery Ltd. asked the men to resume work in the other seams that were not damaged, because of the vital part the coal industry was to the National Service in the War effort. 79% of the workforce reported for duty.

'The spirit shown by the men in making this wholehearted back to work call.' He also expressed his admiration to the rescue efforts and of the colliery manager, and all the rescue workers.

Many manifestations of deep sympathy marked the funerals. Most particularly that of James Bennett, aged 41, and his son Robert who were buried in the same grave. The Father's body, which had been recovered earlier, and because of his severe injuries was listed as unknown. He was only identified by a relative a short time before his sons funeral was to take place. The City Coroner, on receiving a sworn testimony, issued a burial certificate in order that the double funeral may take place. Two of the remaining bodies were recovered, and a special mention was made by the coroner that the bodies of all the men and boys had been recovered in eight days, represented a marvellous achievement which would be appreciated having a knowledge of the dangerous conditions that prevail following an explosion.

Many, many stories of valour and heartache can be told of this terrible disaster, but it would require a tome to do so.

17. The Bevin Boy

In the latter end of the second Great War, coal stocks were running short, due to the insatiable demand to manufacture the implements of war and the acute shortage of manpower. At the beginning of hostilities, a great number of miners' were called up because they had served in the forces pre-war and were in the reserves and the territorial army. Although the miners' were in a reserved occupation, many volunteered for air crew and were accepted because of the great loss of life in the R.A.F. The depletion of the work force was worsened of course by the daily accidents and disasters like Mossfield and Sneyd Collieries. The latter happened on New Years Day in 1942, when 57 men and boys were killed in an explosion. In normal times, due to superstition, hardly any men would be at work on such a day. This fear was put aside and they paid the ultimate price for their country.

The Leader in the Evening Sentinel stated at that time:-

'We have often said that working in the pit was as vital as service in the army. These men have given their lives to King and Country as if they had been fighting with the forces of the Crown'

There was no cheap subsidised coal from abroad that had caused so much anguish to the Miners' in those days before the war. Most of these mines were now in enemy hands. A lesson should have been learned in after years when all the deep pits are being closed.

Ernest Bevin, then the Minister of Labour and National Service devised a scheme to rectify the shortage. All men to be mobilised, would have their future decided by ballot, whether to serve in the armed services or work in the mines. Those selected to work in the mines were called 'Bevin Boys'. They came to North Staffordshire from all walks of life. The rich and the poor, sons of Peers of the realm to the lowest labourer.

And so it was that Geoff Baker came to work in the pit as a Bevin Boy. Geoff was the son of a parson in London and had just left boarding school. He had never worked in his life and now here he was to work in the dirtiest and most dangerous job in the Country. He was appalled at first, because he had set his heart on becoming a marine, but the ballot determined his fate, and on the 24th. January 1944, he arrived at Stoke station on a wet and dismal evening, accompanied by other Bevin Boys and some conscientious objectors. Coaches took them to various land ladies in the Potteries. At first his planned accommodation for some reason or another was not now available, not that she had taken an instant dislike to him, because she never saw him. He remained on the coach until they came to the last port of call, which was in Leek Road, Shelton. This Lady had agreed to take eight. Seven Conscientious Objectors and one Bevin boy and although she had not any room for Geoff, she agreed to take him.

At first he slept on the settee, but found more rest with sharing a bed of another chap who was on nightwork, leaving the bed warm for him when he returned. Geoff went for training at the Kemball Colliery, which was used for training in those days. After a month at Kemball, and classes at the North Staffs Technical College, he was allocated to Norton Colliery. At about this time he changed his digs, thinking it was about time he had a bed of his own. Another Bevin Boy was leaving the area to work in a pit nearer his home town, and he recommended his land lady to him in Waterloo Road, Burslem. She was an excellent landlady and he stayed with her until his discharge. He started to work on the screens at Norton and found it boring, dirty and at times very distasteful. The work entailed separating the dirt or stone from the coal, and now and again his hands inevitably were soiled by excreta, for there was no toilets in the pit in those days, which he was to discover later on. After a month on the surface he was promoted to work underground. he was filled with apprehension at the thought of going 'down under', at the same time he had a feeling of satisfaction that at last he was going to contribute to the war effort.

With his newly acquired snappin' tin, water bottle and helmet he collected his lamp from the lamp house and approached the cage for the first time, wishing that he had brought a change of underpants! Stooping to enter the cage the strange smell of earth, stale sweat, and tobacco invaded his nostrils. Hemmed in on all sides by colliers, who looked askance at this foreign body in their midst. There was a chuckle and some laughter and some words of profanity. A bell in the distance rang and in a trice he dropped, plummeted into the bowels of the earth at some seventy feet per second, the cage rattling and groaning at what seemed to him an uncontrollable speed. His hands sought that part of him that appeared most threatened! The cage slowed down and the lights of the pit bottom loomed into view and the sight of human faces were welcome and he was reassured that he was still of this world. Gulping the stale air he waited for his stomach to return to its rightful place. A that moment he would have agreed to spend the rest of his life down there, rather than ascend and go through it all again on the morrow. He had heard people talk of the 'Big Un' in Hanley, which was far deeper than this, and he thought, 'If thats the case I'm glad I am at Norton, this is deep enough for me.'

Unknown to him, the manager had found out that he was good at playing cricket, having played for his boarding school, and asked him to play for Norton. Whether this had anything to do with it he never knew, but he was given a 'cushy job' as assistant to the surveyors'. So armed with a measuring tape, a ball of string, and a lump of chalk, he determined the position of the roof supports. He strutted about the coal face in overalls and the miners', stripped to the waist and sweating profusely, viewed him with some suspicion, anger and he supposed envy, and would make matters worse by shouting at frequent intervals 'Come on chaps B------k it on', meaning shovel the coal on to the conveyor belt. Life went on splendidly for a few weeks, 'this job will do for me' he thought, but at the same time a twinge of conscience reminded him that he was playing little part in winning the war. One day being bored and waiting impatiently for the time when he could finish the shift. 'What's the time' he asked one of the loaders.

'Near loose it', he replied with a smile.

Geoff was never late when it was time to finish, and he made his way to the pit bottom, where he met the Colliery manager. 'And where the hell dust think they't going'? the manager asked.

'Another shift finished Mr. Steele, one more shift nearer my demob', he answered in his usual humorous manner.

Geoff did not think any more about it until he arrived at the pit the following morning and found a note on his lamp which stated: 'Since you have seen fit to disregard the confidence and trust I have put in you, you will start loading on the Cockshead seam as from this morning'. Signed the manager. The message now was quite clear to him that from this day he had to start work in earnest, with the consolation that at least he was going to do something worth while, but at the same time he couldn't think for the life of him how he was going to cope with it.

It had never occurred to him that you had to buy your own tools. He went to the stores to obtain a pick and a shovel.

'Wots they want?' asked the storeman.

'Well I've come to get a pick and shovel' Geoff said.

'Wots they want wi' a pick an' shovel. Oose it fer?' the storeman asked.

'It's fer mey o'course' replied Geoff trying his best to put his case in the local dialect.

'Wot at they gooin' ter do wi' a pick and shovel?'

'Well' Geoff answered, 'cause ah've got to use it'

Silence ensued for several moments, the storeman trying to take in that this young toff was actually asking him for one of his picks and a shovel and that he was going to use it.

'Well, er well er wots sort er shovel dust want, wot weight'.

Geoff was rather stumped with this question. he was aware that there was different weights in cricket bats, but not shovels.

With some reluctance the bemused storeman handed over a suitable shovel and pick. Geoff took them and turned to go.

'Ere theyst fergot ter sign fer 'em. Thee anna free thee knowst. Theyst gotta pee fer 'em ite a thee weeges. They knowst that dusna?'

'yes I do now' said Geoff with a smile.

Armed with the pick and shovel he made his way to the cage getting surprised looks from the men who knew him.

'Weet they gooing wi' them?' asked one.

'I am going loading on the Cockshead seam' Geoff replied.

'They'? enquired another. 'Ah thote you' were on serveyin' staff.'

'So I was, but it appears I have been given the boot'.

He arrived after a trolley ride and some walking on the face at Cockshead, where he took off his jacket and stripped to the waist.

'Theyt catch bloody noomonia they wut', remarked one of the colliers. 'They atna used ter this sort o' life

One of the firemen came and detailed him to work with Joe Jones a collier, known locally as 'Big Joe' because he was a big man in heart as well as build. Joe took to his prodigy right away and became firm friends. He was very interested in the way Geoff talked and the way of life he had lived, coming from boarding school and being the son of a parson. But within a week he was moved on to work with another collier name Alby, because too much time was spent in conversation. Now Alby was as little as Joe was big. These two men became great friends and long after the war Geoff remained in contact with them until they died. He had tremendous fun with both of them and they invited him to their homes, played cribbage with him in their locals. Many, many years later Geoff said he could write a book or fill several recording tapes about the fun he had had with Big Joe and unashamedly said that he loved him dearly. He recalled one morning arriving on the coal face, and starting to strip off.

'I say Joe. It's frightfully cold this morning'

'Eh surry. Wot did'st see?' asked Joe.

'I said it's frightfully cold this morning'

'Ah', said Joe, 'Ah'll 'ave ter practice that'.

So Joe practiced for several days until he could, parrot fashion, say it very well. One morning, on the coal face, he thought he would try out the mimicry on some of the miners'

'I say chaps, it's frightfully cold this morning'.
They all looked at him as one in amazement.
'B-----s!' they all replied in unison.
Big Joe was very disappointed at the response, for all the effort he had taken to improve his diction and reverted back to his own local dialect.
Geoff remembered very early in his loading days, in fact on the first morning on the face, he thought he would show these chaps what he was made of. The shift started at 7 am and snappin' time was at 11 am and the time to finish was 2.30 p.m Of course the shift was not strictly 7 hours, for there was the travelling time to the face and back which you did not get paid for. He got stuck in, and in his estimation he had loaded more coal than any miner in the coalfield had ever done. He never stopped and was sweating profusely, and the pains in all parts of his body where he had never experienced pain before and he was, to use his own words, 'Absolutely knackered. He started to slow down thinking by this time, with all the effort, that it must be near to snappin' time.
'What time is it'? he asked Joe.
'Bloody 'ell surry, it's only quarter ter nine', replied Joe.
Geoff sat back on his haunches completely exhausted not knowing how he could carry on to finish the shift.
He remembered other men in the pit. There was Big Jack, another tall man, whom he met on the face one monday morning.
Monday morning was always a very unpleasant day because the men would, after a week end of drinking relieve their bowels on shovels, and disperse it on the conveyor belt. The aroma, or to put it stronger, stench, lingered all day and for the refined stomach like Geoff's, took some getting used to.
'Did you have a good time at the week end Jack?' Geoff asked, finding it a bit difficult to breathe without taking the polluted atmosphere deep into his lungs.
'Na', answered a forlorn looking Jack. 'Ah did'na'.
'Why?' Geoff asked.
'Becose ah've bigged 'er anna ah'
Now this was another word that had not entered Geoff's vocabulary, but he discovered that it meant that he had got his girl friend pregnant.
Freddy Mole, and Clive Owen who was a right lad, were other men Geoff remembers, together with Cyril Dodd, Jimmy Tompkinson, Alf Reynolds, George Merideth and many others. George once asked Geoff. 'Wot at gooin' ter do wen thee goost wom'?
'I might go in the church' Replied Geoff.'

'Thees moor money in minin' than the is in vicarin'' George advised him.

'Remuneration is not the prior consideration, George. One is called to that life'. Geoff said.

'They beyin' cowed!' Exclaimed George, 'Ah've 'erd they bloody cowed, but it were never a vicar!'

And then of course there was Sam. Sam was not his real name, but for reasons we will soon discover, might cause some embarrassment, or fame. Due to the conditions the men worked in, there were no niceties of privacy, and private parts were anything but private. Geoff was amazed, and thought that Sam was endowed with the largest he had ever seen or thought possible.

'By Golly Joe', Geoff said to Big Joe, 'Old Sam is well blessed I have never seen anything like it'.

Joe looked at him and smiled. 'Sam, and 'is faither and 'is brother 'ave got a yard betwain 'em'.

Geoff was amazed and looked at Joe in disbelief.

'It's true ah tell thee', said Joe.

As Geoff had never had the pleasure of viewing the phenomenon of the three, measuring three feet between them, he had to take Joe's word that it was a fact.

The twenty minutes allowed for snappin' time Geoff always found interesting. Because Geoff came from another environment in which he was always, 'The Bloody Tory' the main topic was nearly always political.

There soon came a time when Geoff ran out of pit clothes to wear. It is obvious to anyone that nearly any old clothes can be used for work in the pit, so Geoff, to replenish his wardrobe, went home to London during the Christmas Holidays to visit his parents. His mother, being a parsons wife, held, on many occasions, jumble sales in the East End of London, for fund raising and for supplying of clothing for the poor of that area. His mother held up a dinner suit for sale. It was a perfectly good dinner suit and as Geoff said there was not a great demand for such apparel in the Docklands of that Great Metropolis at that particular time, and there were no bidders except for Geoff, who bought it for sixpence, thinking it would go down like a bomb at Norton Colliery.

He arrived a few days later with a brown paper parcel at the pit head baths. He emerged a few minutes later and made his way in the darkness to the lamphouse to get his lamp. Other miners' and lamphouse staff were astounded by the apparition that had entered. No wonder they stared in amazement, there was Geoff complete in his outrageous ensemble, the like of which had never been seen before and never will be again, in the annals of mining. A miner clad in a dinner suit with broad shining lapels, and a white shirt complete with a dicky bow. On his head he wore the compulsory pit helmet, his feet clad in clogs and around his waist he wore a brown leather belt. No one spoke, and you could have herd the proverbial pin drop. Obtaining his lamp he made his way to the pit head. The banksman nearly fell down the shaft in amazement. 'Wwweer the ******* 1ell dust they think theyt ggooin'!' he stuttered.

'Me?' Geoff replied in a nonchalant manner.

'Ah they'! exclaimed the astounded banksman

'Me, oh I've just come from a party and I haven't had time to change', replied Geoff with a twinkle in his eyes.

As the cage descended he heard the amazed banksman utter:

'Well *** mey'! 'That bloody ******* bloke from the south. Wot the 'ell is 'e gooin' ter do next?'

He arrived on the coal face and neatly folded the odd ensemble and put it safely on one side. His masquerade caused hilarious laughter throughout the pit. Even years after when Geoff visited his old friend Big Joe, he would be introduced to Joe's friends, "Ere this is the youth, ah towd yer abite. This bugger. Wore a bloody dinner suit dine th' pit'. Joe would say. With the cold draught of air on a sweaty back, and all the hard work, resulted in Geoff having trouble with his back. He was not the only one with back trouble, it was a common ailment working in the pit, indeed it still is. Geoff went home on a weeks sick leave and as there was little improvement, his doctor told him to have a further week.

On resuming work he was met by Big Joe.

'Weest they ******* bin? 'Weest ******* bin?' They wenst wom fer a wick, and theest bin a ******* fortnaight! Weest bin'?

'I was bad Joe' Geoff replied rather pitifully.

'Theyt o'wees bad they at. Theyt lark Port Vale they at. Theer o'wees bad. Wot's bin dooin' fer money?

Geoff lowered his eyes and took on a look of guilt.

'Well Joe to tell you the truth'

'Ah tell us th'truth wot ever thee dust' demanded Joe.

'You see Joe I was short of money, I was getting desperate so, there was a box in my father's church and written on it was:

'For the sick.'

'******* 'Ell' exclaimed Joe 'Wot sort o' christian at they?'

This was the typical repartee that Geoff remembered and cherished all his life. The humour and camaraderie.

He recalled the day when he wanted to relieve his bowels and he never liked the idea of what the other men did. He knew that there was a bucket at the pit bottom, and it meant that he had got to walk about a mile, but it was preferable, to him, than dropping his trousers, and doing it on his shovel.

'We'at at they gooin"? Asked Big Joe.

'I want to be excused', Geoff said and deliberately used the work 'excused' because his mother used it rather discreetly or:

'Do you want to sit down Geoffrey?'

'I want to go to the toilet' Stressed Geoff.

'Dust want a p*** or s***? Asked Joe.

'I want to sit down'

'Well bloody go 'ere'!

'Where?'

"Ere on thee bloody shovel'

'I cant do it here, it's, its' embarrassing. It's not done'

'Cause it is. Wey o' do it 'ere, they at na goin' ter walk o' that wey over a mile ter the pit bottom just ter 'ave a bloody s***!' Exclaimed Big Joe who by this time was getting rather irate.

'But I haven't any paper', said Geoff trying to make a feeble excuse.

'Yer dunna want any paper, use them wood shavings' retorted Joe.

As Geoff remembers some 50 years later incidents like these left a deep impression on his mind if not on his backside. There was so many memories good and bad. Above all, the friendship and the humour which he revelled in, and being fully accepted when he could chew a twist of 'bacca' without being sick. The bad times like the dirt, dust, graft and the danger. There were many accidents, the one man who had been all through the war, and in a week of starting in the pit was buried by a fall of the roof, and was killed.

Eventually the time came nearer to his demob. Big Joe and all his mates tried to persuade him not to tempt fate and to finish early.

'They'st worked dine 'ere na fer nearly foer years and apart fer a few bosted fingers marks on thee 'ands and scars on thee back ter give thee a few colliers' marks theyst come through this lot unscathed, so call it a dee an' dunna tak' any risk' 'No', replied Geoff with some conviction. I'm going home with a full wage packet, I'm going to get my full five shifts in'. When it came to the last week, they all refused to have him on the coal face and he was found a job on the haulage.

On the last day having handed in his lamp for the last time and showered and changed, he made his way to the canteen to have his usual cup of tea. He became aware that there seemed to be more men there than usual. After a bit of a speech the men presented Geoff with a smoking cabinet for putting tobacco and pipes in. 'Dunna tell every other Bevin Boy, cos thee'll all ****** want one' Shouted Alby. Geoff treasures that cabinet to this day and gives it pride of place in his drawing room in his home. There is a small brass plate on the cabinet inscribed: 'To Geoff from his mates at Norton Colliery'. It says it all, Mates from Norton Colliery, if they had put colleagues, to me he said, it would not have seemed appropriate. Mates was just the right word.

Other good things happened to him whilst he was in North Staffordshire. He met Billy Briscoe, who played for Port Vale for many years, and kept the Black Boy public house in Cobridge, and who is still going strong at 96. They were playing in a cricket match at Sneyd Green and Bill invited Geoff home for supper, where he met Marjorie, Bill's daughter, who he fell in love with and subsequently married in 1949. He recalled his good fortune, and said that if he had not won that ballot by the Ministry of Labour in 1943, this would have never happened. Neither would he have had the unique experience of meeting and working with the miners' of North Staffordshire, for whom, together with all the people of the Potteries, he has the highest regard and esteem.

Geoff Baker has a constant reminder of these experiences having named his house in Kent, 'Joffers'. This was Big Joe's nick name for him, so Geoff's old friend is never forgotten.

18. Pit Humour

The miner is well known for his humour, dry, droll and at times absurd and to quote some extracts from the Silverdale Post:- The miner is unique, for he has the ability to hold his own in any company when it comes to telling a joke, or, with a face as calm as an innocent child, he will lead his listeners on, finally leaving them wide eyed with some impossible finish to his story, leaving them with the realization that they have well and truly been taken for a ride.

There is a wealth of humour to be found underground, despite the danger, dirt, dust and graft. Such as the warning chalked on a low placed girder or strut. 'Duck or Grouse' told its own tale, or the story that comes to mind of the man who came out of the pit holding a pad to his head. 'What's the matter Joe'? asked the banksman when Joe stepped out of the cage at the surface.

'I was walking along the level when a girder 'it me!' Joe replied. Sharp as a flash the banksman retorted, 'Well Ah dunna know abite they lad, wey 'it it back wi thee yed!'

The miner who returned to work after a days absence, knowing that he would have to run the gauntlet of jibes and droll comments, particularly if the man was newly married.

'Rusty Clog tips.' 'wunner 'er get off thee shirt flap?'

'Is thee back bad?' Nothing was sacred.

One subtle story which has been purloined by the T.V. comics and others, is the man being paid a shift too many, said nothing. During the week the office staff discovered the error and the extra shift was stopped from his next pay. He was furious and stormed into the office demanding to know why. 'You didn't come back last week when you were paid a shift too many', said the clerk. A look of surprise and bewilderment on the mans face, Changing in a moment to one of a pundit. 'No I didn't!' he exclaimed, 'I will allow for one mistake, but two weeks together wants seeing into'.

A Colliery Cameo By Ex Deputy Geoffrey Valco.

Whilst oft I lie in vacant and pensive mood, my inward eye flashes back to my coal mining days in North Staffordshire and, there I see, glinting, clanging, ringing, that wonderful invention, the underground telephone. I would therefore like to put pen to paper and record a typical shift in one of the collieries in order to enlighten the readers of the tremendous uses of the instrument.

The face of the man standing close by to a point where the No. 2 face haulage joins on to the main haulage, presents an almost seraphic, or one might say, a drooling look as he watches the endless stream of full tubs pouring out of No. 2 gate level to be sent on their way to the pit bottom, one can see at a glance that he is some one of authority by the power that seems to emanate from his person, also the fact that he is wearing Knicker bockers and leggings, he is an Overman.

Suddenly No. 2 rope jerks, stops, jerks and the haulage engine shudders to a grinding halt. An amazing change of expression comes over his face, his features contort into a snarling grimace. With a muttered curse, he leaps forward to the telephone with the speed that would put a Gazelle to shame. Foam has appeared to the corners of his mouth, his eyes threaten to protrude from their sockets. Snatching up the receiver with his left hand and with his right hand rotates the handle at a terrific speed. If the telephone had been a generator, enough motive power would have been raised to supply Silverdale, Knutton, and the bigger part of Chesterton for all its power and light requirements. An harassed deputy, screaming, sweating, rushes forward to answer the telephone situated near to No. 2 face, he has fallen down twice in the process as he picks up the receiver with a trembling hand, the voice so loud in intensity and volume nearly bursts his eardrums.

'Wot the bloody hell is gooin' on dine theer?'

'Waive got a mess twenty yards up gate', replied the deputy rather apprehensively.

'Well get the bloody rope gooin', dust want mey ter come dine an' do the bloody job fer thee?' shouted the irate overman. 'It wunna bey long na Jacka, eh's just knocked on nah', answered the deputy with a sigh of relief.

Serenity reigns once more, the coal flows, the tubs rattle their tortuous way, the deputy relaxes and pauses to regain his breath casting a furtive glance now and then at the now silent telephone as if expecting some ogre to leap out of the mouth piece.

The overman resumed his seraphic outlook and his whistling 'You are my honeysuckle, I am the bee', life is good.

Four hours later and a mere trickle of coal is coming out of No. 2 at the main junction. Again that rapid change of personality comes over the overman, this time his spittle is deluging down the mouthpiece like some waterfall cascading over the brink of its fall. He picks up the telephone waits impatiently for the deputy to answer it.

'Now wot the bloody 'ell is up dine theer. Cosna they bey left on they own or summat?' the overman demands.

Thoughts are running through the deputy's mind which if came true, would be of tragic consequences for the overman.

'The face belt brock, the fitter is on it nah', the deputy answered in a voice hardly higher than a whisper.

'Well get the bloody facemen on to it, instead of sitting on their backsides doin' nowt an' get a bloody move on', the overman bellowed.

'Reight o' Jacka'.

And so passes another peaceful shift in the coal mining industry.

Owd Codger's Views
By Eddie Cation

The Nerve Senter and Improvin me Dicshun

Ah was a little perterbed abite missin last wicks news letter, but threw surkumstances beyond mah control ah wanna in time fer it. Tother dee ah stud agen that theer control room, ah'd call it the 'Nerve Senter'. Me sel, an them lads want a U.C. as big as 'Yoorope', that theer fones never ite of their 'ands. Ah funt ite one thing, theyne got noo watches in th' pit, is eyes ar never of th' clock wi' chaps askin' fer the time, it keeps them lads fair busy. Ah've come ta th' conclooshun the gaffer wants to geer 'em up wi' a talkin' clock, lark them on th' G.P.O. It ud save them lads a bit a time. Ah've sane summat else as wants doin' an ah'll 'ave a werd wi' 'Leeker' abit it cause it must cum under the safety ah'm thinkin'. Wot abite sum paddin' on them fones, cause wot ah've sane abite it, them lads wun get a luvely collyflower ear, that fone is never awee from their lug 'oles. Me sel ah think a bit o' paddin' on th' ear peece will save them fellas lug 'oles a bit. Seems ah'll see th' gaffer abite it, eh's a very understandin' bloke.

Anywee them lads are the 'Nerve Senter' of th' pit, even Bycycle Jack noes that wen 'e gets all 'is informashun off Tessa on the tannoy. Tokin abite Tessa, 'eh approched mey tother wick an' sed, 'Wey dustna they goo nate scoo' ter improve thee dicshun'? Ah lucked at 'im as though eh was daft. But eh were raight yer no, Anna yer sane sum o' those big werds ah've bin usin', ah think my Inglish is improvin' a lot. Ah asked me Tuter ah ar were gettin' on, cud eh see any improvement in me dicshun? The chap just lucked at mey an' scratched 'is yed an' sed, 'They keep at it lad, theyt win in the'end. Dun ya no ah went wom as prewed as anthin', 'eh did give me a lot a 'art, ah wunna let 'him dine. Ah'll conclude this eer note, so dunna ferget lads luck afta yersells.

The Tote Blank Ball

Ah want ter thank yo' lads fer gettin' stuck inta this eer competition. Ah belave wey're owdin' ah own so fer.

Ah've bin towd Aggie an Kit ah fer joinin' the Caterin' Union. Ah bin towd they're the best dish weshers in the canteen an' their 'ands ah as soft as a babbies bum. T'other dee ah saw a feller walkin' abite th'bonk wi' a stick, ah were towd eh was a very wurried mon. Thee reckon the Tote Blank Ball, its fifty quid dropped on 'is leg an brock it. Harpy is fair glad it anna bin drawn ite yet. The last time it cum ite, it made the lad proper bad. The Sister was fair worried abite 'im. They got Ray rind wi' a quart bottle o' brandy, ah've erd tell eh's as tite as a monkeys ear. Ah saw Leeker in the' canteen eh were purrin' lark a big tum cat. Eh towd mey wey won owdin' ah own so fer in th' national wey'd bey o'rate if wey keep it up ah think, eh's rate prowd of 'is sel so dunna let's breek is 'eart lads. Keep it up an dunna take risks an' wey'ne cum threw o'rate an' ah'll see ya on th' fly paper.

Hot Pants

Weet fer it lads, an' ya 'erd the latest, wey're in fer a raight treat. After a ton o' trouble, the canteen gaffers got us sommat nice ter eat wen yer cum up th' pit. 'Ers got sum HOT PANTS fer us, ah dunna no ar much thee cost, but 'er said theyne bey a cheenge from cakes. Any wee, they'ne luk nice amung them tater pies. Wunna thee? But ah've bin towd yer munna eat em if thee ar cowd. Nat this fella nose abite fost aid and eh towd me if ya eaten em cowd, yown get a belly ake, so jest bey warned will ya? Did ya no wayne got a mon at th' pit, 'eh's best breen wesher in th' area, this lad con toke. Ah'll tell yer ar good 'eh is. If Jesus come fer a job on th' sheerers, 'eh'd toke 'im in 'aving a job sniggin fer 'Arry Allman. Ah no one thing 'arry wud luk after 'im, 'Eh'd see abite sum wick end werk fer 'im an' 'eh wudna goo short of nanties. Ah dost bet thee any money 'Arry wud 'ave 'im tackin' snuff in noo tarme at owe, 'eh'd luk after 'im 'Arry wud. Eh's a good lad is ah 'Arry!

Mey an' Mah Lady

It were a nice naight, so mey an' mah lady went ite fer a woke an' ah tuk 'er rinde Kent's Lane Bonk. Wey wun amazed at o' thase changes gooin' on, yo conna tell th' owd place any moor. Theyne ripped up o' th' reels in th' medda an o' the coals goo in bunkers na. Us saw'em loading a train an wey won surprised ah they dun it. That sure is progress an ah tuk 'er ter the new drift mine an' it tuk mey awaile ter get it throo to h'er an' tell 'er o' abite it. 'Er lukked at mey an'sed 'Dust remember them dees wen thee used ter cum wom in thee dirt lad'? 'Wey'd jost got married, an' thee mam got us a little ise dine the rode. Dost no lad them wun 'appy dees them wun'. 'Er laffed an' then said, 'Dost remember that dee wen they wost 'avin' a bath on the'arth an' 'er frum next dooer walked in as ah wus weshin' thee back? 'Er let ite wun yell an' run ite agen. Wanna 'er face red? Ah bet er wuddna blush na, wud 'er owd lad?' Ah lukked at 'er an' smiled an' sed, 'Ah them were the dees Aggie owd wench.' 'Er said, 'Things ah a lot better na, thee goost werk clane an cum wom clane dunna thee? Wot's this eer P.L.A. ah've red abite?' 'Power Loadin' Agreement ah towed her, it's a new wage scale theyne brung in owd wench.'

It tuk me a good weyle ter get it threw to 'er, weyle wey walked rind th' bonk. Er lukked at me an' sniggered an' sed, 'Thee in much power in thar loader theese dees is there owd lad'

Ah bosted ite laffin yer never noo wot thase wimmin ar thinkin' dun yer?

'Ah cud do wi' a pint Aggie', ah said. 'Er lukked at mey an' sed, 'Cum on then, ah've got a bob er two in me poss'. 'Er tuk me arm gooin' dine th'rode. Wey sut inth club and ah sed ter 'er, 'They'te raight abite the P.L.A. Aggie'.

19. A Few of The Most Valiant

John Harold Rhodes, was born in the village of Packmoor, Stoke-on-Trent on May 17 1891. he worked as a miner at Chatterley Whitfield colliery from 1905 to 1911 at which date he joined the Grenadier Guards. he returned to Chatterley Whitfield in 1913, and was called to the colours on the outbreak of the first World war in 1914. Joining his regiment, the Grenadier Guards, went to France with the First Expeditionary Force. In 1915 he was awarded the D.C.M. for rescuing several wounded men and bringing back valuable information whilst under fire. In August 1917 he was awarded a bar to the D.C.M. The only Grenadier to gain the D.C.M. twice. The French also noted his bravery by awarding him the Croix de Guerre.

On October 9. 1917, he was awarded the Victoria Cross, the highest accolade for valour. Unfortunately, John Harold Rhodes never saw his medal, nor experienced the jubilation for such an heroic warrior, for he died of his wounds on November 27 1917 at Fontaine Notre Dame in a later skirmish with the enemy.

The citation of his V.C. reads:-

No. 15122 Lance Sergeant John Harold Rhodes of 3rd. Battallion Grenadier Guards. For most conspicuous bravery when in charge of a Lewis Machine gun section, covering the consolidation of the Right Front Company, he accounted for several of the enemy with his rifle and by his Lewis gun and seeing three of the enemy leave a 'pill box', he went out single handed through our own barrage and hostile enemy machine gun fire and effected an entry into the 'pill box'. He there captured nine of the enemy including a forward observation officer, and brought them back together with valuable information.

For all his bravery, awards and sacrifice for his country, the honour he brought to his native North Staffordshire, John Harold Jones for many years had been forgotten until in 1984, the Grenadier Guards Association provided the well deserved memorial, a commemorative plaque, and is situated at his last place of employment, Chatterley Whitfield Colliery, which was a mining museum.

They went with songs to the battle, they were young,
Straight of limb, true of eye, steady and aglow.
They were Staunch to the end against odds uncounted,
They fell with their faces to the foe.

They shall not grow old, as we that are left grow old;
Age shall not weary them, nor the years condemn.
At the going down of the sun and in the morning
  We will remember them.

Diglake

On the 9th. March 1895, Queen Victoria, presented William Dodd, the undermanager, with the Albert Medal.

John Boulton, John Johnson, John Watts, Joseph Bateman, and Amos Hinkley received the Royal Human Society Award.

New Hem Heath

The Carnegie Hero Fund Medals, were presented to Harry Bickerton and Thomas Gleaves, who rescued six men who were over come by carbon monoxide and at the risk of their own lives attempted to rescue another twelve before being overcome themselves.

Minnie

There were so many Most Valiant of Men at this disaster, all the men in the rescue teams were awarded the North Staffs Colliery Owners medal.

The Chief Inspector of Mines paid tribute to Frank Halfpenny, who surviving the blast of the explosion, and without hesitation although he was in dense smoke walked inbye to telephone the manager on the surface as to the conditions below. Most men would have made for the shaft and their own safety, but he walked inbye to see if he could render aid, regardless of the risk to himself. He was awarded the Edward Medal by King George V.

Three years after the tragedy, the heroism enacted by many others, in particular the rescue teams, were recognised. Carnegie Trust medallions bearing the inscription:

'He serve God best who mostly nobly services humanity'.

These were presented together with certificates and monetary grants. Awarded with £25 grants were:-

Dr. William Megaw, Walter Farrington, Henry Summer, William Hancock, John Holding, Frederick Perkin, James Farrington, Thomas Machin, Edward Warren, Harry Stanier, William Stanier, John Moores, Frank Halfpenny, Charles Greatbach, and Thomas Brockley.

Midland Rescue Team No. 3

Chatterley Whitfield No. 4 Rescue Brigade

Those awarded £10 Grants:-

Thomas Genders, William Kesteven, Charles Dean, Frederick Jones, William Jones, George Clarke, William Machin, John Bailey, Arthur Roberts, Earnest Hankey, William Guest, C.H. Weaver. and Joseph Smith.

Holditch (Brymbo)

Rescue team, Ezra Clarke, (Captain). James Gleaves, Joseph Woodcock, Frederick Taylor, Hector Doorbar. That at Congress International de Sauvetage, held in Paris, Awarded the Colliery team the Grand Prix International du Courage, offered by the President of the French Republic consisting of a large Sevres Vase and a medallion of Honour.

(This fine vase was presented to the North Staffs Rescue Station, and given pride of place in the foyer.

Rowland Bennett

Hanley Deep Pit

Rowland Bennett, Manager, earned the Edward Medal, the Miners' V.C. and his name inscribed on the Carnegie Hero Fund Roll of Honour. His Courageous conduct averted a tragedy when a serious accident occurred underground in 1935.

Great Fenton

Richard Jones, sacrificed his life to save his mates at the No, 2 pit Stafford Coal & Iron in May 1941. His name was inscribed on the Carnegie Hero Fund Roll of Honour.

Medal awarded to Harry Bickerton and Thomas Gleaves

20. Gas Outburst at Norton Colliery

Of all the perils that beset those who choose to work in the mining industry, none are more feared than the noxious gases fermented in the distant past by the decaying vegetation of the carboniferous age. Unseen and insidious, they are the cause of many fatalities and injuries due to explosion, accidental inhalation and other reasons. Chief among these gases and the most common is methane. Constant vigilance is needed to ensure that its harmful effects are neutralised by different methods. By far the best of these methods is to ensure a good ventilation system by means of a constant current of fast flowing air dispersing the gas as it percolates from the strata.

At Norton Colliery, where I spent most of my working life, conditions in this respect were not so bad. Except for an occasional headache by inhaling an odd whiff or two, I was never unduly worried by this hazard. That is, until one day in 1965, when its power and virulence was demonstrated in an unusual and terrifying manner.

At that time I was working on 5's face in the Bullhurst seam. I was one of a team of men whose task it was to help support the roof by means of strip packing after the coal had been extracted and the coal face advanced by a few feet. Because of the system of work, we were required to do this on a 'split' shift and this meant that for a short period of time, we were the only men in the district, being under the supervision of a single deputy. On this particular day, shortly after the day shift had left at 1.30 pm, my workmate George and myself, were engaged in constructing a buttress pack at the bottom end of the face. The rest of our team of ten men and the deputy were near the top end of the face about 150 yards away from us. The face machinery and level conveyors were still and except for the usual underground noises that we were well accustomed to, every where was quiet. Suddenly, we became aware of a strange hissing noise that became louder and louder and appeared to come from further up the face. We looked at each other questioningly, then, a series of loud cracks and bangs prefaced an ominous rumbling. Realising that something badly untoward was happening, we ran to the comparative safety of the nearby intake level and within seconds the noise increased to a deafening roar like that of thunder overhead and the whole area began to shake and tremble. Many thousands of tons of rock and coal were displaced by this mini earthquake, the large 15 feet steel arches supporting the intake roof groaned and squealed in protest as they strove to resist the mighty forces being imposed on them. We retreated full of fear, further away down the level to what we hoped would be a safer position. The noise reached a crescendo and then to our great relief gradually died away and all became quiet.

Finding that the ventilation was still good and that we were both safe, we went back and at the level switchgear, turned off the electricity supply to the face as a precaution. Meanwhile an anxious management team arrived on the scene alerted by Stan our cool and competent deputy. Stan had withdrawn the other miners' to safety, because, as we learned later, they had been in far greater danger than George and I.

An investigation revealed that the earth movement had been caused by a huge undetectable concentration of gas under the floor of the coal face. This suddenly erupted and the enormous pressure shattered the structure of the floor, destroying the stability of the Dowty hydraulic support props over a long length of the face. This sudden withdrawal of support caused the earth movement and did tremendous damage, both to the face, machinery and ancillary equipment. The return heading was filled with a dangerously high concentration of escaping gas which could have had very serious consequences had it not been prevented by swift and decisive action. It took weeks to repair the damage and to bring the face back into full production. But this was infinitely preferable to what the consequences could have been. Some retribution can be expected from time to time for mans' exploitation of the earths mineral resources, but in this case, thankfully, human beings did not have to pay the price.

21. Women of Stout Heart

It would be inappropriate of me not to mention the women of the Valiants for without them where would they be.

These women of stout heart and strong back who nurtured and worried about their men, expecting no reward and never received any. Her concern was that her man was fit, strong and healthy to provide sustenance for her family and a roof over their heads. Even in these modern times, with computerised wash days, pithead baths, micro wave cooking, she is still concerned when her man leaves for the pit, worried about all the pit closure and if in the near future he will have no job. She was by his side in the strikes of '12, '21, '26, '72, '74 and 84/85, fighting and striving for her family. But do not let us for get these women of stout heart and try to imagine what it was like in the 'Good Old Days'.

A typical family in 1920. Husband and five sons all working in the pit. In the time when there was a disaster every year and sometimes two. Fatalities were frequent and accidents occurred daily. What would this woman be thinking of when they left her early each morning and caressing the youngest, a boy of 14. What her thoughts would be, would she ever see them again or would they come home crippled never to work again. She had to dismiss these morbid thoughts and get on with her chores. The Wash boiler to light and stoke with coal and start the weekly wash with tub, dolly peg, scrubbing brush and soap. The clothes washed, scrubbed and rinsed were fed into the mangle. No job this for the sickly and weak. No dryer to finish but a line in the back yard and, if the weather was inclement placed on the rack in the living room and hoisted up to the ceiling.

Time was pressing, there was the beds to make, the bedroom floors to scrub on their hands and knees, the parlour and living room would have to wait until the next day, for it was time now to get the men's dinner ready for when they came home from the pit.

Potatoes to peel and vegetables to prepare. The rest of the Sunday joint to be warmed in the oven heated by the coal range. The tea brewed and the place made ready for her dirty tired men. The boiler filled up with water and stoked again to make sure she had plenty of hot water for them to bathe.

Home they came one by one, the sound of the clogs clip clopping in the yard. A nod and a smile to welcome them home. Thank God they are all here safe and sound. Well, that is except Charlie he's got a bandage on his hand.

'Wot 'ave yer done to yer 'and lad' she'd say with concern in her voice, 'It inna much mam, ah've just bosted me fingers, That's o' Charlie would reply.

A quick wash of the hands in the sink in the back kitchen. Bowls of lobby or mouth watering meat and potato pie dished out on the table and she would watch and smile when her men would appreciate the food she had prepared and they finished the lot and looked around for more. Her husbands pipe would be filled and a spill made ready for lighting. The tin bath brought in from hanging on a nail in the yard and put in front of the living room fire. Pans of hot water ladled from the boiler in the kitchen and laboriously emptied into the bath. A skirmish by the eldest lads to see who was to be first, whilst the youngest, Charlie, would have found a haven to rest his weary body, on his knees with head resting on his mother's rocking chair fast asleep, knowing that he being the youngest would be last to bathe. The eldest lad having won his right to be first was stripped to the waist and, whilst he washed his front parts his mother was scrubbing his back and so on until the last one was clean and changed and then troop into the parlour where they would nap, read a paper and talk about the happenings in the pit. No rest for her, the mother and wife, the pit clothes to shake in the back yard and placed neatly in the hearth. and if wet a place to be set for them to dry in front of the fire ready for the next day. Young Charlies fingers to be inspected cleaned, lint with ointment applied. Bath taken away and stowed on the nail in the back yard, the boiler cleaned and the ashes removed from the fire. The days washing nearly done and the earlier tested ready for ironing. The solid cast irons were placed on the fire, no electric, thermostatically controlled steam irons then, but removed from the fire and a spit to prove their temperature, a wipe with a cloth and she would iron away until time for tea.

'Wot's fer tea'? an urgent cry from the parlour.

'Pig's yed brawn' she would reply, 'It'll bey on th' table in ten minutes'.

She had brought the pigs head from the butcher for sixpence and a standing order for one a week. Her family liked her home made brawn and besides it was a cheap nourishing meal, 'It only cost a tanner a meal fer the whole family', she would say 'And another meal the next dee for the owd mon. Eh loves the pigs ears dipped in batter an' fried'.

She had religiously cleaned the head a few days earlier, soaked in salt water and hung up in the back kitchen for a few days. Then into a big black cast iron saucepan and boiled until all the flesh came off. The meat was then minced with mincing machine which was clamped to the table. When the saucepan had gone cold she would skim the fat off and mix it with the

The tin bath brought in

pork flesh along with a few herbs and put it in a basin turned upside down on a plate. In a day or two, when set, she would remove the basin and it would appear to be like a nice jelly. She would then serve it with some crab apple jelly, which she had preserved the previous autumn. Tea over, wash the dishes and continue ironing until late on in the evening. There was the snappin' to make ready for next morning. Rounds and rounds of bread, loaf upon loaf spread with either beef dripping or margarine and sandwiches of bananas, cheese, sometimes bacon made wrapped in paper or put in snappin' tins. Sticks and coal ready on the hearth for the fire next morning. Weary, she would retire to bed to be awakened next morning early about 5 am by the knocker-up tapping on the window with his/her long pole. Then the long hard day would start again and at the back of her mind, the constant anxiety that her men would return home safe and sound. In the days of private ownership, disasters were frequent. Everyday fatalities and injuries were common place. Illness caused by dust and water, nystagmus that made men in their prime, unemployable, to be nursed for the remainder of his short life by their uncomplaining women of stout heart, and no hand out from the State, no invalidity pay, no income support, nothing. Can anyone imagine the anguish of the wife and mother, when in one disaster her whole family, in one terrible stroke of fate, were wiped out. Nine of her men in one household, husband, seven sons and a brother. The curtains of mourning were never lifted again in her house and she lived on only a few months after that terrible day, alone, grieving and almost penniless.

Donations received from charity did not go far for the women folk of the village of Senghenydd, Glamorgan when the Universal pit exploded killing 439 men and boys on the 14th. October 1913 causing the depletion of nearly all the male members of that village.

Compensation was minimal in those days if at all. The owners insurance doctors treated the claimant like a workshy malingerer, and there was no hand out from the state for the widow or her children, they had to survive the best they could with a small pittance from the miners' benevolent fund or the relief provided by the local council via the ratepayers. Her pride and joy was the range or fire place, the large gleaming black cast iron implement set in the chimney breast, it was the heart of the home. It gave warmth, comfort, a place to cook, bake and dry the clothes. A haven to sit by when the days toil was o'er, a place to dream on, look into the flames and see pictures and the imagination soar. It became a shrine to kneel to and clean until, like a mirror, see your image. It demanded in return a sacrifice of time, sweat and a tin of Zebra grate polish and to be fed, its hunger insatiable, with coal.

The deprivation and despair they suffered in the 1921 and 1926 strikes trying to sustain the family on hardly anything. The degrading weekly visit to the pawnshop with the few pitiful belongings until there was nothing left. The anguish in her heart seeing her children barefoot, their clothes in tatters and hungry. The bailiffs men taking her last few possessions. The many 'Moonlight Flits' and the last straw, the workhouse. These women of Stout Heart did not desert their men in their hour of need, struggled and some died by their side.

22. List of Known North Staffs Mines Since 1875

Acres Nook	Harecastle	Dukes Farm
Adroswell	Holly Wall	Dale Hall
Brown Lees	Harriseahead	Downfield Side
Brownsfield	Hallfield	Eastwood
Black Bank	Hayes Wood	Froghall
Booths Wood	Ipstones	Falls
Boon Hill	Jamage	Fox Holes
Bignall Hill	Kerry Hill	Ford Gren
Bells Hollow	Kents Lane	Glebe
Brook House	Kidsgrove	Gainmore
Bucknall Church	Lane Ends	Greasley
Blackstone	Lady's Well	Heathcote Road
Broadfields	Leycett	Hazelwood
Chell Heath	Lancasters	Hem Heath
Chapel Lawn	Major Barn	Hill Top
Cold Lea	Millfield Gate	Head o' th' Lane
Consall	Adderley Green	High Field
Coalpit Hill	Anchor	Heath House
Callow Hill	Bucknall	Hanley & Bucknall
Chatterley	Brindley Ford	Ivy House
Comer Road	Brown Hills	Joiners Square
Dales Green	Blakelow	Kingsley Holt
Diglake	Birch House	Knutton Farm
Daisy Bank	Bradley Green	Lowlands
Eaves Lane	Botteslow	Lawton
Foxt Wood	Blurstone	Little above Park
Florence	Bunkers Hill	Little High Carr
Fenton Park	Biddulph Valley	Moor Side
Furlong	Bradeley	Mill Field
Gilmoor	Chell Green	Apedale
Goldenhill (Longton)	Chell Meadows	Ashwood
Grange (Cobridge)	Cheadle Park	Bentilee
Gibbons Bank	Clough Lane	Bradfields
Greasley Side	Cronhill	Brocton
Havelock	Common Side	Boyles Hall
Hanley Hayes	Cobridge	Bang Up
Holly Wood	Clewley Park	Ballbrook

Berry Hill
Bathpool
Birchenwood
Bells Hill
Chell
Church Lane
Childer Play
Central
Clough Hall
Cross Flats
Chesterton
Dilhorne
Diamond
Dukes
Engine
Foxfield
Foremans
Fair Lady
Far Green
Glass House
Goldenhill
Grange (Audley)
Golden Dale
Grubbers Hill
Hill o' Lea
Hazel Cross
Hamil
Hollinswood
Hulme Valley
Hanley Deep
Holditch
Indpendent
Jackfield
Kemball
Knutton Manor
Lockwood
Lower Ash
Lillydale
Lawn
McEllins

Miles Green
Alderhay Lane
Ashworth
Bank
Biddulph
Boothen
Burley
Ball Lane
Bycars
Bank Top
Birtles
Baileys
Black Bull
Camp
Cherry Eye
Clarkes
Chalky
Clanway
Crackley
Coppice
Delphouse
Dingle
Foley
Forge
Foxley
Good Hope
Greenfields
Gorsty Bank
Greenhead
High Lane
Hall End
Homer
High Carr
Hall Fields
Hall
Harrison
Jumping
Knutton
Kidswood
Levels

Litley
Lily
Lunts
Meir Hay
Mill Hayes
Mitchell Wood
Meadow Stile
Mossfield
Mousecroft
Merry Hill
New Chaple
Newfield Farm
Nabs Wood
Newfield
Oak Tree
Old Grove
Old Field
Packmoor
Parkhall
Peacocks Hay
Ridgeway
Ravens Lane
Racecourse (Cheadle)
Rowhurst
Red Street
Stone Trough
Sutherland
Sky Lark
Scotia
Silverdale
Turnhurst
Thursfield
Talke Green
Tunstall
Ubberley Hill
Wetley Moor
Weston Coyney
Winpenny
White Star
Woodshutts

Woodstock
Water Hayes
Wood Lane
White Hill
Miles Green
Mosey Moor
Meir Heath
Millbank
New Red Hall
New House
New Hem Heath
Norton Old Butt Lane
Old Hays Wood
Provident
Park Hall
Rookery
Ravens Cliff
Rosemary Hill
Rising Lark
Stone Road
Swindle Hill
Shaffalong
Slappenfield
Slippery Lane
Trubshaw
Tetchlence
Tinkersclough
Talke o' th' Hill
Victoria
Woodhouse Lane
Wonder Pits
Woodmain
Woodlands
Wood Side
Wood Farm
Wolstanton

Well Street
Yield Hill
Moody Street
Mow Cop
Mary Hill
Miry Wood
New Haden
Nelly Dale
Northwood
New Hayes
Oldcote
Outclough
Pennyfields
Park House
Park Farm
Radfields
Racecourse (Hanley)
Racecourse (Silverdale)
Ryecroft
Red Cross
Snoper
Stanfield
Speedwell
Sladdenhill
Sandbach
Tubbscroft
Target Wood
Townsend
Tower Hill
Valentine
Whiston Eaves
Windy House
Woodhouse
Woodhouse (Audley)
Wheel & Bbye
Wellington

White Barn
Wood Lane
Mays
Moss
Minnie
Madeley
Newbold
Nelson
Nabs
New Pool
Oak
Oxford
Plants
Pinnox
Pear Tree
Recovery
Red Hall
Rectory
Shawe
Sherriff
Sands
Swan
Sneyd
Top Falls
Town Tileries
The Grove
Victory
Wood Burn
Winnie
Will Field
Whitfield
Watkins
Wedgwood
Woodhead

23. Pit Disasters From 1855

The following is a record of colliery disasters in North Staffordshire from 1855. Not less than five killed.

Date	Colliery	Location	Killed
25th May 1855	Oldfield	Longton	7
29th Jan 1859	Bycars	Burslem	5
2nd Mar 1864	Brookhouse	Hanley	5
1st Mar 1865	Clough Hill	Kidsgrove	5
13th Dec 1866	Talk o'th'Hill	Newcastle	91
11th Nov 1867	Homer Hill	Fenton	12
7th July 1870	Silverdale	Newcastle	19
12th Jan 1870	Leycett	Newcastle	8
12th Mar 1872	Berryhill	Stoke	6
22nd Dec 1872	Silverdale	Newcastle	8
18th Feb 1873	Talk o'th'Hill	Newcastle	18
24th Dec 1874	Bignal Hill	Audley	17
30th Apr 1875	Bunkers Hill	Kidsgrove	43
6th Jul 1875	Jamage	Chesterton	5
6th Apr 1876	Silverdale	Newcastle	5
23rd Mar 1878	Apedale	Newcastle	23
12th Sep 1879	Leycett	Newcastle	8
21st Jan 1880	Leycett	Newcastle	62
7th Feb 1881	Whitfield	Tunstall	21
16th Oct 1883	Leycett	Newcastle	6
10th Apr 1885	Great Fenton	Stoke	8
20th Jun 1885	Apedale	Newcastle	9
18th Oct 1889	Mossfield	Longton	66
2nd April 891	Apedale	Newcastle	10
14th Jan 1895	Diglake	Audley	78
25th Nov 1911	Jamage	Chesterton	6
15th Jan 1915	Minnie	Halmerend	9
25th Feb 1915	New Hem Heath	Chesterton	12
12th Jan 1918	Minnie	Halmerend	155
18th Dec 1925	Brichenwood	Kidsgrove	7
2nd July 1937	Holditch	Newcastle	30
21st Mar 1940	Mossfield	Longton	11
1st Jan 1942	Sneyd	Burslem	57

24. Major British Pit Disasters From 1850

Date	Pit and Location	Death Roll
12 November 1850	Houghton, Durham	26
15 March 1851	Nitshill, Renfrewshire	61
18 August 1851	Washington, Durham	35
20 December 1851	Warren Vale, Rawmarsh, Yorks	52
10 May 1852	Middle Dyffryn, Glamorgan	26
10 March 1890	Gwendreath, Glamorgan	26
20 May 1852	Cappull, Preston, Lancs	36
24 March 1853	Ince Hall, Wigan, Lancs	58
18 February 1854	Ince Hall, Wigan, Lancs	89
15 July 1856	Cymmer, Rhondda, Glamorgan	114
19 February 1857	Lundhill, Yorks	189
31 July 1857	Heys, Ashton under Lyne, Lancs	40
2 February 1858	Bardsley, Ashton under Lyne	53
11 December 1858	Tyldesley, Leigh, Lancs	25
3 March 1860	Burradon, Durham	74
1 December 1860	Black Vein, Risca, Monmouthshire	142
16 January 1862	New Hartley, Northumberland	204
19 February 1862	Cethin, Galmorgan	47
8 December 1862	St. Edmunds's Main, Yorks	59
6 March 1863	Coxlodge. Northumberland	26
17 October 1863	Morfa, Port Talbot, Galmorgan	34
16 June 1865	Tredegar, Monmouthshire	26
20 December 1865	Cethin, Cyfartha, Glamorgan	34
23 January 1866	Park Lane, Wigan, Lancs	30
12 December 1866	Oaks, Yorkshire	361
13 December 1866	Talk o'the Hill, Staffs	91
8 November 1867	Ferndale, Pontypridd, Galmorgan	178
28 November 1868	Hindley Green, Wigan, Lancs	62
26 December 1868	Haydock, Lancashire	26
1 April 1869	High Brooks, Wigan, Lancs	62
10 June 1869	Ferndale, Pontypridd, Glamorgan	53

21 July 1869	Haydock, Lancashire	59
15 November 1869	Low Hall Wigan, Lancs	27
14 February 1870	Morfa, Taibach, Glamorgan	30
10 January 1871	Renishaw Park, Chesterfield Derby	26
24 February 1871	Pentre, Pontypridd, Glamorgan	38
6 September 1871	Ince Moss, Wigan, Lancs	70
5 October 1871	Seaham, Durham	26
28 March 1872	Lovers' Lane Atherton , Lancs	27
7 October 1872	Morley, Yorks	34
19 April 1874	Astley, Dukinfield, Cheshire	54
30 August 1875	Bunker's Hill, Kidsgrove, Staffs	43
6 December 1875	Swaithe Main, Barnsley, Yorks	143
11 October 1877	Pemberton, Lancs	36
22 October 1877	Blantyre, Lancs	207
9 March 1878	Unity Brook, Kersley, Lancs	43
7 June 1878	Wood Pit, Haydock, Lancs	189
11 September 1878	Abercan, Monmouthshire	268
13 January 1879	Dinas Middle Pit, Pontypridd	63
2 July 1879	Balntyre, Lancs	28
21 January 1880	Leycett, Newcastle, Staffs	62
15 July 1880	Balck Vein, Risca, Monmouth	120
8 September 1880	Seaham, Durham	164
10 December1880	Naval Steam Coal, Penygraig	101
7 February 1881	Whitfield, Tunstall, Staffs	25
19 December 1881	Abram, Wigan, Lancs	48
16 February 1882	Trimodon Grange, Durham	68
18 April 1882	Tudhoe, Durham	37
2 May 1882	Baddesley, Atherstone, Warwicks	32
7 November 1882	Clay Cross, Derby	45
7 November 1883	Moorfield, Altham, Lancs	68
2 March 1885	Unswroth, Durham	42
18 June 1885	Clifton Hall, Lancs	178
23 December 1885	Mardy, Pontypridd, Glamorgan	81
2 December 1886	Elemore, Fence Houses, Durham	28
18 February 1887	National, Pontypridd, Galmorgan	39

28 May 1887	Udston, Lanarkshire	73
19 April 1888	St. Helen's Cumberland	30
5 September 1889	Maurice Wood, Midlothain	63
16 October 1889	Mossfield, Longton, Staffs	66
6 February 1890	Llanerch, Monmouthshire	176
10 March 1890	Morpha, Port Talbot, Glamorgan	87
26 August 1892	North's Park Slip, Tondu, Glamorgan	112
11 April 1893	Great Western, Pontypridd, Glamorgan	63
4 July 1893	Combs, Dewsbury, Yorks	139
23 June 1894	Albion, Cilfynydd, Glamorgan	290
14 January 1895	Diglake, Audley, Staffs	78
27 January 1896	Tylorstown, Ferndale, Staffs	57
30 April 1896	Micklefield, Yorkshire	35
24 May 1901	Universal, Senghenydd, Glamorgan	81
10 March 1905	Cambrian, Clydach Vale, Glamorgan	33
11 July 1905	National, Wattstown, Glamorgan	119
14 October 1906	Wingage Grange, Durham	25
4 March 1908	Hamstead, Staffordshire	26
18 August 1908	Maypole, Wigan, Lancashire	75
16 February 1909	West Stanley, Durham	168
29 October 1909	Darran, Glamorgan	27
11 May 1910	Wellington, Whitehaven, Cumberland	136
21 December 1910	Number 3 Bank Pit Hulton, Lancs	344
9 July 1912	Cadeby Main, Yorkshire	88
14 October 1913	Universal, Senghenydd, Glamorgan	439
12 January 1918	Minnie Pit, Halmerend, Staffs	155
20 October 1919	Levant Tin Mine, Cornwall	31
5 September 1922	Haig, Whitehaven, Cumberland	39
28 July 1923	Maltby, Yorkshire	27
25 September 1923	Redding, Falkirk, Stirlingshire	40
30 March 1925	View Pit, Montague Coliery Northumberland	38
1 March 1927	Marine, Monmouthshire	52
29 January 1931	Haig, Whitehaven, Cumberland	27
20 November 1931	Bentley, Yorkshire	45
12 November 1932	Garwood Hall, Lancashire	27

22 September 1934	Gresford, Denbighshire	265
6 August 1936	Wharncliffe, Woodmoor Colliery Yorkshire	58
2 July 1937	Holditch, Newcastle, Staffs	30
10 May 1938	Number 1, Markham, Derbyshire	79
28 October 1939	Valley Field, Fife	35
1 January 1942	Sneyd, Burslem, Staffordshire	57
15 August 1947	William, Whitehaven, Cumberland	104
26 September 1950	Cresswell, Derbyshire	80
29 May 1951	Easington, Durham	81
18 September 1959	Auchengeich, Lanarkshire	47
28 June 1960	Six Bells, Monmouth	45
21 October 1966	*Aberfan, Glamorgan	144

*Although not an underground mining disaster, it can be attributed to the effects of mining. It should be remembered as one of the worst in mining history causing the horrible death of 116 innocent children who, were at school on that day. On the 21 October 1966, at 9.30 am the colliery waste tip that was situated on a steep hillside above the village of Aberfan, became an avalanche and enveloped the school and several houses under 45 feet of mud.

There were more disasters of course, the list depicts not less than 25 killed.